RCA **CRD** RESEARCH PUBLICATIONS

CRD PROJECTS
GENERAL EDITOR GILLIAN CRAMPTON SMITH
EDITOR GILES LANE

RESEARCH PUBLICATIONS DESIGNED BY PAUL FARRINGTON
PRINTED IN THE UK BY GEOFF NEAL LITHO

FIRST PUBLISHED IN 2001 BY THE
COMPUTER RELATED DESIGN RESEARCH STUDIO
ROYAL COLLEGE OF ART
KENSINGTON GORE
LONDON SW7 2EU
UNITED KINGDOM
WWW.CRD.RCA.AC.UK/RESEARCH

BRITISH LIBRARY CATALOGUING-IN-PUBLICATION DATA: A CATALOGUE
RECORD FOR THIS BOOK IS AVAILABLE AT THE BRITISH LIBRARY.

ISBN 1 874175 32 2

THIS PUBLICATION HAS BEEN GENEROUSLY SUPPORTED BY
THE EUROPEAN COMMISSION (THROUGH THE I3 INITIATIVE)
AND INTERVAL RESEARCH CORPORATION.

Royal College of Art
Postgraduate Art & Design

THE PRESENCE PROJECT

RCA CRD PRESENCE TEAM
ANTHONY DUNNE & **WILLIAM GAVER** WITH
BEN HOOKER, SHONA KITCHEN & **BRENDAN WALKER**

WRITTEN BY
WILLIAM GAVER

DESIGNED BY
BEN HOOKER

RCA **CRD** RESEARCH

THIS BOOK DESCRIBES THE COMPUTER RELATED DESIGN
DEPARTMENT'S RESEARCH FOR THE PRESENCE PROJECT.
THIS WAS ONE FACET OF A LARGER PROJECT INVOLVING:

DOMUS ACADEMY, MILAN
HELEN HAMLYN RESEARCH CENTRE, LONDON
HUMAN FACTOR SOLUTIONS, OSLO
INNOVATIVE DEVICES & ENGINEERING FOR AUTOMATION, PISA
NETHERLANDS DESIGN INSTITUTE, AMSTERDAM
CRD RESEARCH, ROYAL COLLEGE OF ART, LONDON
SCUOLA SUPERIORE S'ANNA, PISA
TELENOR, OSLO

WITH THANKS TO

G. BERKEL, S. BORSBOOM, MR. BROWN, L. CHRISPINA,
MR. AND MRS. VAN DAAL, MS. DRIESSEN, R. FROIS,
ROSINDO FROLIJK, V. GOMEZ, MR. AND MRS. HARSONO,
MR. HUNSEL, CELIA DE JESUS, I. KELLY, E. KLAS,
MS. LEEMHUIS, MAINTZ, H.A. MEENG, P. MESMAN-SILOOY,
NEL NIESING, A. OBISPO, J. PATRICK, MAURITS SCHMIDT,
C. SCHUTTE, J.C. STEIJN, MR. SUHADIJANTORO, NEL VENTE,
MR. VERHOEF, E.J. WIJNGAARD AND J.P. VAN WINSEN,
WHO LIVE IN THE BIJLMER

MAJ BIRGIT RØRSLETT, ELSAKARIN RINGKJØB, MÅLFRID BRU,
BODIL BRØGGER, ANNE-MARI SIMERS, ELSE ZIMMER DAHL,
EDVIN SAETHER, INGEBORG VON HEIMBURG, GUNNAR BAY,
KIRSTEN BAY, EVA BALKE, BERIT MICHAELSEN,
INGER LAMPE SØHOLT, JON SVERRE DAHL, ARNE RØNNING,
BARABARA ROBØLE, KARI NORDBYE, EBBA REIMERS,
HILDE MOWOINCKEL, GERD SVENNEBY AND
ELSA WAAGENES UDBJØRG, **WHO LIVE IN OSLO**

CASATI MARTA, FIORINI BRUNO, FUSI MARISA,
MACELLONI VASCO, MAZZEI FLORIS, SIMONCINI GIORGIO
AND TURINI CARLA, **WHO LIVE IN PECCIOLI**

PAUL BENCZE, JANNEKE BERKELBACH VAN DER SPRENKEL,
SIDSEL BJØRNEBY, ESTHER DE CHARON DE SAINT GERMAIN,
SIMON CLATWORTHY, DANIELLE VAN DIEMEN, SASKIA 'T HART,
KAY HOFMEESTER, CECILIA LASCHI, ELENA PACENTI,
MARCO SUSANI AND JOHN THACKARA

JAKE BEAVER, BARBARA BRUGOLA, SAMANTHA DYER,
PAUL FARRINGTON, RAY GRIFFITHS, HARVEY HARDAWAY,
JON HIRSCH, LEIGH HIRST, SARAH PENNINGTON, FIONA RABY,
ANNE SCHLOTTMANN AND GILLIAN CRAMPTON SMITH

Contents

Foreword

The big problem with information technology is that it tries so hard to be rational.

By contrast, humans are happy to be rational only part of the time. Most other times (apart from the fact that they sleep so much) people operate in very different modes: of daydreaming and pondering; of joy and melancholy; of hope and of despair ... apart from all the other subliminal states of which, most of the time, we are not even aware. Now, all of these I would call the non-rational. To be clear, by non-rational I do not mean irrational – that is a word that (because of the rationalists) has taken on a pejorative expression of impetuousness, rashness or absurdity, which the non-rational cannot be reduced to, but can clearly embrace.

Because all information technology systems have started out in life with a big ration of the rational, the logical conclusion seems to be that, indeed, we should work towards a new and perfect world – a technocracy directed by the empty ethos of machines. Projects under the i3 research initiative – and in particular PRESENCE – rejected this purely positivistic absurdity, that along with the development of the computer, has been furiously promulgated over the last 50 years. However, rather than taking a 'neo-Luddite' stance, i3 aspired to start from human-centred notions to see how new technology could be invented and interwoven in that context. It asked for ways of supporting (and not replacing) everyday people doing everyday things: of supporting creativity and imagination, of friendship and community, having a chat, of ...

Now, if anything of this 'speaks' to you, then you should read this book – if not, then perhaps you should quickly put it away. What it offers is one account of an exploration of how to do the seemingly impossible – of how to investigate, reflect and design for the non-rational. This, I believe, is just at the tip of a very big iceberg that many will explore in the future.

Cultural Probes, park benches in Amsterdam, neural networks, radio soundscapes, as well as a small village in Tuscany, are amongst many of the intriguing topics covered in this visual book. In doing so, it explores the creative potential of co-design, as well as the potential of human ambiguity. In result, it points to how people in communities can start expressing and experiencing themselves in new and subtle ways, and how – paradoxically – information technology can help.

Jakub Wejchert
Future and Emerging Technologies Unit, European Commission*

*The opinions expressed in this foreword are those of the author and do not necessarily reflect the position of the European Commission.

Introduction

As technology increasingly pervades our everyday lives, many people find themselves ambivalent about the digital revolution. Current technologies tell stories about ourselves that are difficult to reject – who would deny wanting to be more effective, to communicate better with friends and family, or to keep up with the latest innovations? Yet current products don't tell the whole story. Endorsing some values while neglecting others, technology seems to seduce us into becoming a kind of people we don't always want to be.

This book describes a project, called Presence, that investigated ways technology can be used to increase the presence of older people in their local communities. Rather than taking the obvious route of addressing older people's problems, we sought to offer new opportunities, to amplify existing pleasures, to create new situations for communication and insight. We explored how technology might tell stories and support values different from those currently recognised in research, industry, and the marketplace.

Our design methods were inspired, in part, by the contemporary arts, a foundation quite different from the scientific tradition used in most of the technology industry. We embraced ambiguity, for instance, as leaving room for exploration, encouraging imagination, and allowing people to project their hopes and desires onto the products of our design. Subjectivity was valued as well: by advocating our own interests and desires as well as those of the older people, we encouraged a dialogue about possible futures. We based our designs on the older people's situations, but extended them in our imaginations to create new technological narratives that filtered and built on aspects of their lives. This approach, and the experimental techniques it engendered, allowed us to work both playfully and purposefully, breaking the boundaries of prevailing scientific approaches to address new values and emotions.

This is a book about process, then, suggesting new ways that designers can engage with people, envision speculative futures, and realise them. It is also a book about technology, and how it might reflect more complicated aspects of our lives than it currently does. It is a book about older people, and our perspective on the opportunities they might grasp and how they might relate to the world. Most fundamentally, however, this is a book about ideas – evoking, communicating, developing, and instantiating them in the form of prototype designs.

THE PRESENCE PROJECT / The Presence project was a two-year investigation of innovative interaction techniques for increasing the presence of older people in their local communities.

Presence was one of an original thirteen projects funded by the i3 (Intelligent Information Interfaces) initiative of the European Union's Esprit programme on information technology. In seeking to address the implications of technologies merging into everyday life, i3 represented an experiment in European funding, explicitly recognising the importance of human and societal factors as well as technological advances. Thus it encouraged participation not only of the usual players – computer scientists, human factors specialists, and cognitive psychologists – but also a wider set of contributors, including designers.

We joined with colleagues from seven other organisations in four countries to form Presence. Our team from the Computer Related Design department at the Royal College of Art was one of two design teams; the other came from the Domus Academy in Milan, Italy. Five research teams, located in Norway, the Netherlands and Italy, were already involved in projects with local older people. Finally, Design Age Network, also located at the Royal College of Art, and the Netherlands Design Institute, in Amsterdam, served as resource organisations, providing years of experience of designing for older people on the one hand, and administrative and publishing support on the other.

The Presence group formed about a year before the project started, to discuss how new technologies might improve the lives of older people, and we submitted a proposal in 1996 which was ultimately funded in early 1997. The plans were broad and open: we knew little more than that we wanted to find ways to encourage older people to become more engaged with their communities, using a variety of methods from traditional human-factors and user-centred design to more artistically inspired design approaches.

We do not attempt a full account of the Presence project here. Instead, we focus on our role as speculative artist-designers in the project, using unconventional techniques and proposing unusual designs to address the lives of older people. A more comprehensive account of the project may be found in *Presence*, a book published by the Netherlands Design Institute.

APPROACHES TO AGING / In taking on a project dealing with older people, we were aware of trends that made it an important endeavour – the 'greying' of society, the difficulty of funding care and services as the proportion of the population in work decreases, the increasing social isolation older people face with the breakdown of the nuclear family, and so on.

At the same time, the danger of such a project was that it would lead to 'worthy' designs, focused so much on solving problems that the results would lose any possible joy or interest. Not only would such designs become uninteresting to us as designers, but, we thought, to older people as well. By emphasising only the negative aspects of their lives, such designs would manifest a kind of 'benevolent ageism' reinforcing perceptions of older people as frail and needy. At worst, such designs could imply undesirable roles for the older people, having an effect diametrically opposed to our original intentions.

Thus we set out to challenge stereotypes of the elders from the outset of the project. We reminded ourselves of the large number of culturally powerful people – artists, businessmen, writers – in their seventies or eighties. We remembered stories our grandparents told us, for instance about gambling at illegal drinking parties, which emphasised that older people are not necessarily 'nice' any more than they are needy. Through stories like these, we sought to bridge the gap between young and old, to recognise the continuities between our experiences and those of older people.

In challenging stereotypes, we also undermined assumptions about the proper way to work with older people. Rather than making our design process simple and supportive, we realised that we could challenge the older people, provoking them to join in a process of imagination and speculation that might lead to new ideas and opportunities.

Throughout the project, our working hypothesis that older people do not need to be protected or cosseted was repeatedly confirmed. At each stage of the design, the elders responded to provocations, challenges and speculations with curiosity and imagination. Typically, in fact, we and our local partners were more hesitant than they were. One of the lessons we learned from the project was to respect our elders – and not in the typical, somewhat condescending, sense of the term.

THE SITES / Central to the structure of the project were the three communities with which our research partners were already involved. Rather than designing for a generic concept of 'older people,' our ongoing encounters with these groups allowed us to know them as individuals living in particular cultures.

Peccioli, near Pisa in Italy, is a small Tuscan hilltop village. Built in medieval times, small winding streets lead through stucco buildings overlooking the surrounding countryside. Local elders are happy there, but younger people are increasingly leaving the village for larger cities. A project was already underway to provide a social centre for the elders, which might also provide medical and other support services.

The Majorstua is an affluent district of Oslo, Norway. Our initial impression was of clean streets and comfortable shops; the people are educated and well off. The local elders had formed an Internet club in the local library, where the computers were also available for the general public, and often used by younger people. The local government, we were told, was interested in using the Web to increase local democracy, but their initial attempts had not met with much interest.

The Bijlmer, finally, is a large planned housing community south of Amsterdam near Schipol airport. Built in the 1970s in an attempt to lure inner-city workers to more verdant surroundings, it failed due to poor transport and financial difficulties. It has since become the first home for many immigrants to the country, but is also one of the Netherlands' most notorious areas, with high unemployment, drug abuse, and crime.

Our initial knowledge of the sites was limited to demographic and anecdotal evidence from the local researchers, and impressions gained from brief visits to the sites. It was clear from the outset that the three sites complemented one another: from south to north, rural to urban, educated to uneducated, affluent to poor, bucolic to stark, they represented a wide range of the situations in which people grow old.

THE STRUCTURE OF THIS BOOK / The structure of this book mirrors the three broad phases – beginning, middle and end – of the project. Key to Presence was its trajectory of opening and focusing a space of designs. The first year was spent envisioning a wide range of design possibilities with the elders that might play meaningful and useful roles in their lives. These possibilities were focused during the second year, until ultimately working prototypes could be built and tested.

In this book, we start by discussing how we got to know the people for whom we were to design. Then we illustrate the range of design concepts we developed and explored with them. Finally, we show how we focused our ideas into a small set of instantiated prototypes that we could try out.

In accord with our tactics of subjectivity, ambiguity, and provocation, we present this material in an open way for readers to experience and extend as they see fit. Text is included as a framework, but most of the job of describing the project is done through imagery. We include a series of brief notes about topics such as narrative, radio, and neural nets as a way of hinting at the conceptual concerns that informed this project. The links between these topics and the description of the project are left unspecified, however: our discussions of these issues are intended to be resources rather than prescriptions.

THE PRESENCE SITES SPANNED URBAN AND RURAL, BOURGEOIS AND WORKING CLASS, NORTHERN AND SOUTHERN EUROPEAN EXPERIENCES.

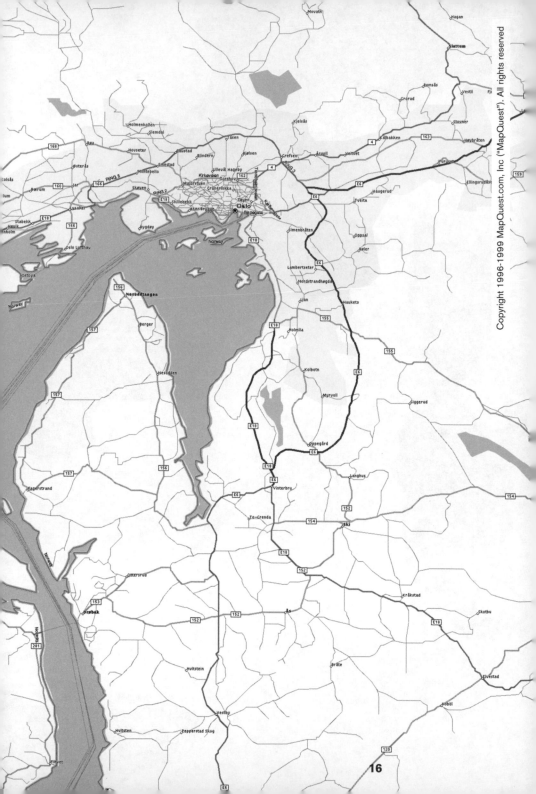

16

Deutsche Bucht

Helgoland

Harwich–Hamburg

Amsterdam–Kristiansand (IX–XI)
Amsterdam–Göteborg (IX–V)

Harwich–Göteborg

Kingston upon Hull–Rotterdam

Sankt Peter-Ording
Büsum
Cuxhaven
Wilhelms-haven
Bremer-haven
Bremen
Stade
Buxtehude

Wangerooge
Langeoog
Norderney
Juist
Borkum
Norden
Emden
Aurich
Oldenburg
Delmenhorst

Groningen
Leeuwarden
Assen
Meppel
Zwolle

Terschelling
Ameland
Schiermonnikoog
Texel
Den Helder
Alkmaar
Zaanstad
Haarlem
AMSTERDAM
Utrecht
Gouda
Leiden
DEN HAAG
ROTTERDAM

Nijmegen
'S-Hertogenbosch
Eindhoven
Helmond
Venlo
Roermond

Middelburg
Vlissingen
Terneuzen
Bergen op Zoom
Antwerpen
Gent
Brugge
Knokke-Heist
Zeebrugge
Oostende
Nieuwpoort
Dunkerque

NEDERLAND

Osnabrück
Bielefeld
Herford
Münster
Dortmund
DÜSSELDORF
ESSEN
Wuppertal
Krefeld
Duisburg
Paderborn
Kassel
Minden

Great Yarmouth
Lowestoft

GREAT BRITAIN

17

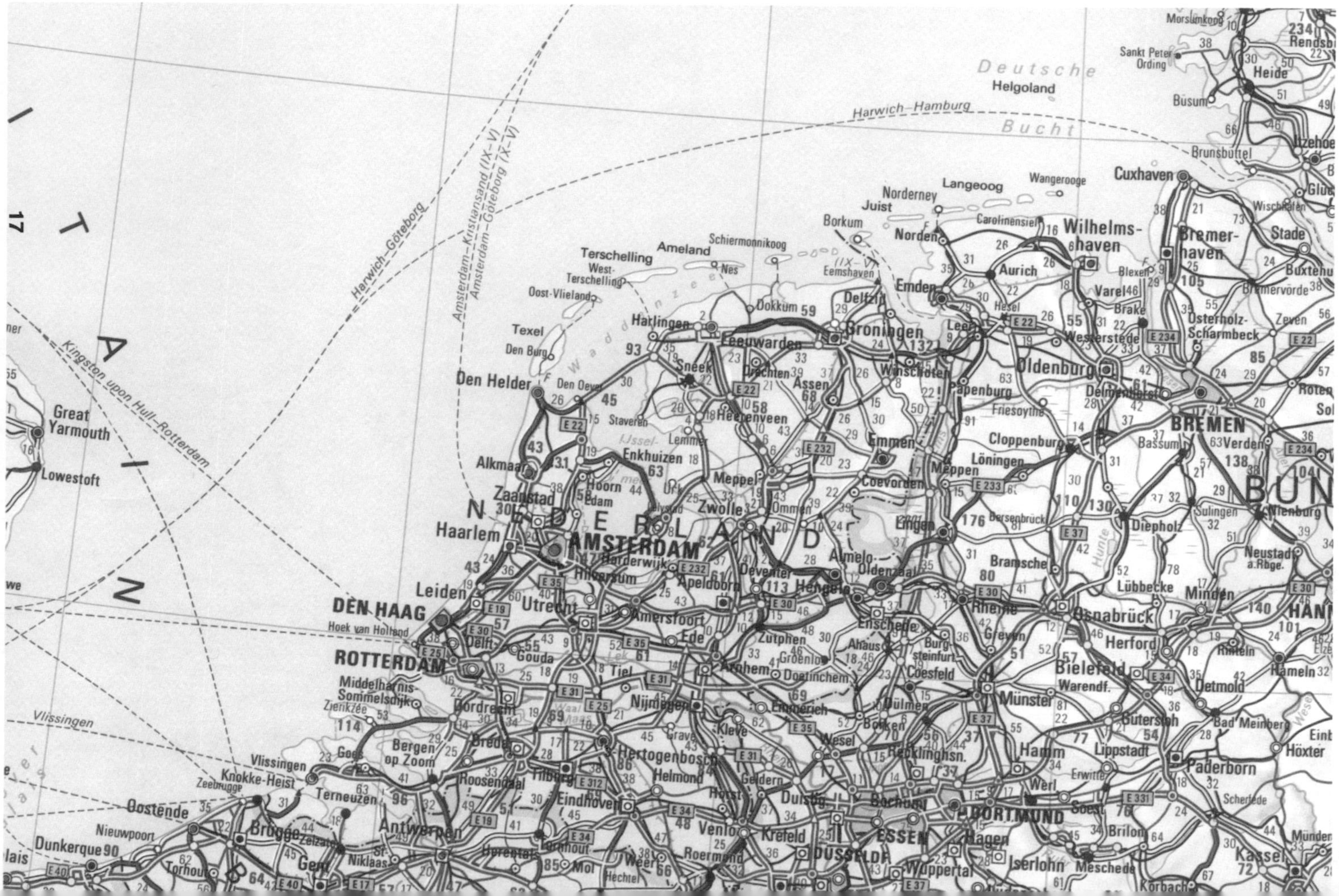

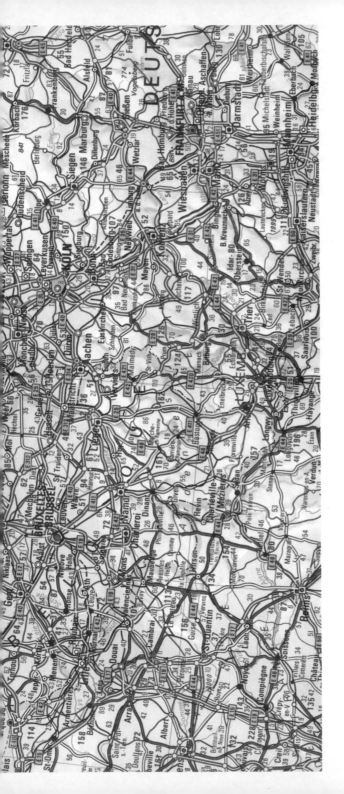

18

Cultural Probes

The very different characters of the three sites in Peccioli, Oslo, and the Bijlmer struck us immediately during the brief visits we made at the beginning of the project. Their physical settings, cultures, and the personalities of the older people combined to give each place its own identity, impossible to confuse with the others. Given this, pursuing generic designs that would be relevant for all three sites seemed inconceivable to us, as they would inevitably undervalue the particular situation in any one. Instead, it seemed clear that our designs should respond to each community separately.

It was obvious, however, that short visits would not allow us to understand the different communities in depth. We had neither time nor budget to make longer stays, and traditional methods, such as questionnaire studies or focus groups, seemed too impersonal to give us the empathic understanding we required. The Cultural Probes grew out of our feeling that we had to explore new methods in order to approach the sites.

MATERIALS / The Probes were packages of diverse materials distributed to older people in each of the three communities, with invitations to respond over time as they pleased. Our intention was to design the Probes to create interesting situations for the older people, giving them opportunities to tell us about themselves and their communities on the one hand and, on the other, hinting at topics we found interesting.

The core materials used in the Probes included postcards, maps, a camera and a photo album. Postcards combined open-ended questions with evocative images to invite discussion. A mundane medium for the dissemination of artistic imagery, postcards demand only the most casual of writing. They allowed us to ask a wide range of questions in a relaxed way: 'What advice or insight has influenced you?' 'What is your favourite device?' 'What use are politicians?'

Maps printed in the form of envelopes were also included in each Probe package. Inspired by the Situationists' psychogeographical maps, we used various requests to get the older people to indicate the emotional topography of their communities – local landmarks, where their friends lived, places they found intriguing or dangerous, and so on. These were indicated with stickers, either coloured or printed with images, that we included with the maps to allow easy annotation.

Each package also contained a disposable camera, repackaged to remove it from its commercial origins and link it with the other materials. A variety of requests were printed on the back of the camera, asking the older people to take pictures such as the view from their window, the clothes they would wear that day, and things they found beautiful, ugly, desirable, or boring. We asked the groups to use any remaining film to simply take pictures of things they thought would help us know them better, allowing them to choose what we should see.

The final element of each probe was a photo album with the request to 'tell us your story in six to ten pictures'. This encouraged the older people to send us their own photographs or clippings, which we copied and sent back to them. When questioned about what we meant by 'your story', we deliberately left the request vague, interested in seeing how they would judge the relative importance, say, of their personal history, their families, or their current activities.

The Probes evolved through experimentation in the three sites. For instance, in Oslo, the site where we first tried the method, a number of ideas either didn't work or weren't appropriate for the other sites. Drawing and annotating landmarks in the local neighbourhood proved difficult for the group, prompting us to develop methods using stickers to annotate the maps. Newspaper stories sent by the older people were revealing, but translating them required more effort than the results were worth. Finally, asking them to use an included kitchen timer to remind themselves to record the website they were browsing every ten minutes or so produced interesting results, but the idea was difficult to apply to the other sites. These methods could be pursued further in future projects, but in dealing with the three Presence sites the core materials we developed seemed easiest to use and most informative.

INSPIRATION NOT INFORMATION / The Probes were designed as an alternative to more traditional forms of user research. We were sceptical about using the methods we already knew for several reasons. Traditional methods seem to set up a sort of game, with implicit rules limiting the relationship between researcher and researched to one addressing controlled content areas. For instance, enquiries intended to inform technology development tend to get answers based on what people already understand about technology, limiting ideas both about new technological possibilities and the activities they might support.

Traditional methods also foster constrained roles for participants. Theory-based methods, for instance, can encourage researchers to treat users as patients, with symptoms or complaints subject to expert diagnosis and description. More participatory methods, on the other hand, suggest that researchers act as servants, offering technological expertise without questioning the basic assumptions behind users' expressed desires. Either alternative serves to hide both the researcher and the people they research: known genres, they have 'rules' allowing both sides to present themselves as they want to be seen. In trying less controlled and predictable tactics, we hoped to get beyond the public face of the older people and their communities, and to reveal ourselves in the process.

Dissatisfied with the methods we knew, then, we started exploring other ideas for creating a conversation between the local groups and ourselves. Realising we didn't want comprehensive information about the communities so much as inspiration for our designs, we felt free to try experimental methods to intrigue the older people, eliciting responses from them that might reveal aspects of their lives to us. We drew inspiration from the tactics used by Dada and the Surrealists, and, especially, from those of the Situationists, whose goals seemed close to our own.

A loose collection of provocative requests, we thought, might provide multiple ways to tap into the lives of the older people. In addition, the diverse materials could be left behind so the older people could engage with them at their own pace, sending us occasional clues from afar, like the data sent back from an unmanned spacecraft or a surgical instrument. With these ideas in mind, we began to design the Probes.

GIVING AND RECEIVING / Each step of the process, from the materials to our presentation, was designed to disrupt expectations about user research and allow new possibilities to emerge. We gave the Probes personally to about ten older people in each site, who greeted them like gifts as they unwrapped them and examined their contents. We stressed that the Probes were an experiment on our part, one that we knew might not work, and assured them that their participation was voluntary and that they didn't have to complete everything. If some of the materials didn't make sense, we said, then send them back, ideally with a note telling us what didn't work. Throughout, we sought to enlist their help in exploring this novel method, and to stress that the fundamental concern was that it should provide them with opportunities to tell us about themselves.

Giving the Probes in personal meetings wasn't our original plan, but in hindsight appeared a crucial part of the process. It allowed us to explain the materials, indicate what our intentions had been, and stress that they were experimental. Being present also seemed to subvert preconceptions of researchers as detached authority figures, and encouraged the older people to identify with what we were trying to do as designers and researchers.

The Probe items were designed to be sent back to us separately: the cards were addressed and stamped, the maps folded into envelopes, and the camera and album also came with mailing envelopes. The three visits were spaced over several months, and returned items appeared in the post for about six weeks after each visit. This meant that new materials flowed in continuously over an extended period of time.

As we sorted through the masses of returned maps, cards, and photographs, strong and differentiated views of the three sites began to emerge. Some items acted as beacons for us: a photograph of friends at an Italian cafe, a map of the Bijlmer with extensive notes about the 'junkies and thieves' in the area, a joke about death from Oslo. They seemed to capture particular facets of the cultures, symbolising important issues clearly and capturing our imaginations.

The return rates from the groups added to our impressions of their differences. The Oslo group returned almost all the materials, and seemed enthusiastic and diligent. The Bijlmer group returned a bit more than half the materials; they seemed less convinced by the project, but willing to engage in tasks they found meaningful or provoking. Finally, the Peccioli group returned less than half the materials, despite being enthusiastic when they received them. We took this as a sign that they were well meaning but happily distracted by their daily lives – an important factor for our designs.

We did not design the Probe materials to enable comprehensive analysis, but rather to provide us with glimpses into the lives of the older people and their communities. In this they succeeded beyond our expectations. In addition to the hundreds of photographs, maps, and cards we received, providing a myriad of idiosyncratic hints about the lives and concerns of the older people, the Cultural Probes acted as an introduction, forming a relationship of mutual experimentation that lasted throughout the project.

The approach we developed with the Probes could be used in many different situations, but we are sceptical about developing a formal methodology from them. The results might be beautiful, but as heartless and superficial as an advertising brochure. Instead, the Probes should be seen as embodying an attitude towards research. Their experimental, even risky nature contributed as much to their success as the particular materials we used. On the one hand, it ensured that both the groups and ourselves were aware of the potential of failure, and tried hard to make the Probes work. On the other, it made the process enjoyable, both aesthetically and socially, as we joined to explore the older people's lives and communities.

THE CULTURAL PROBES WERE PACKAGES OF MATERIALS DESIGNED TO ELICIT REVEALING RESPONSES FROM PARTICIPANTS. THE PROBES PROVIDED RICH REMINDERS ABOUT THE TEXTURES OF THE THREE SITES.

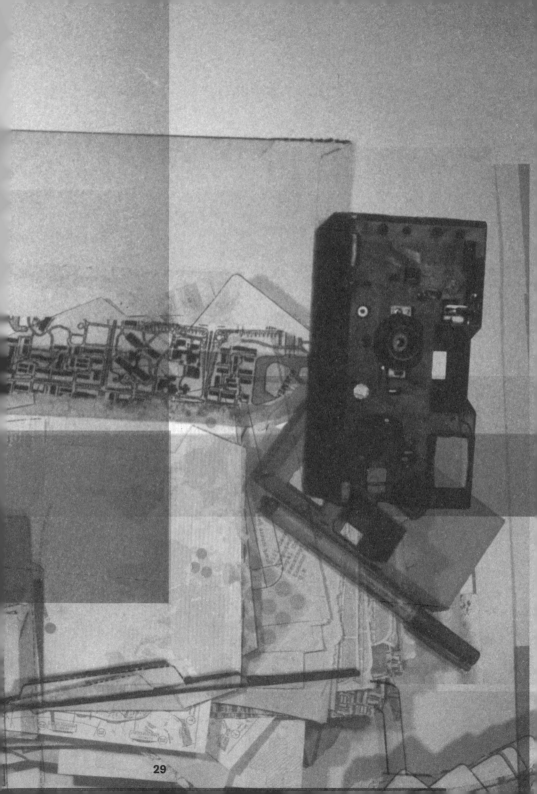

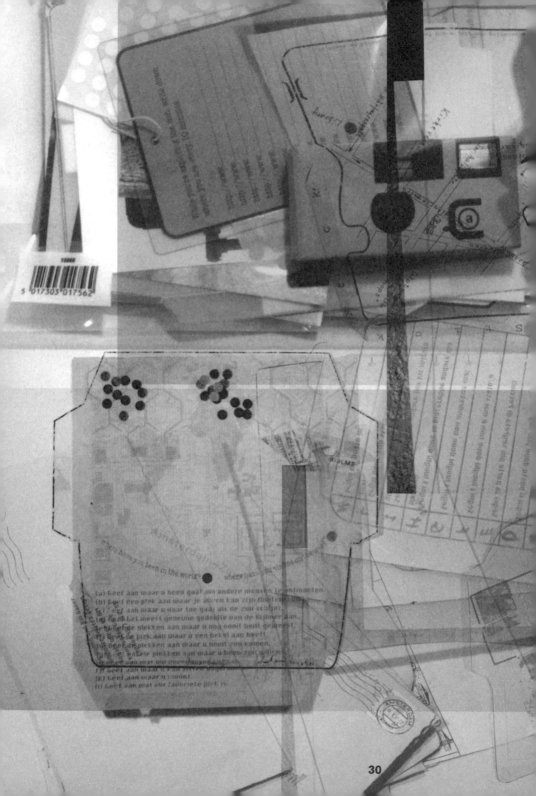

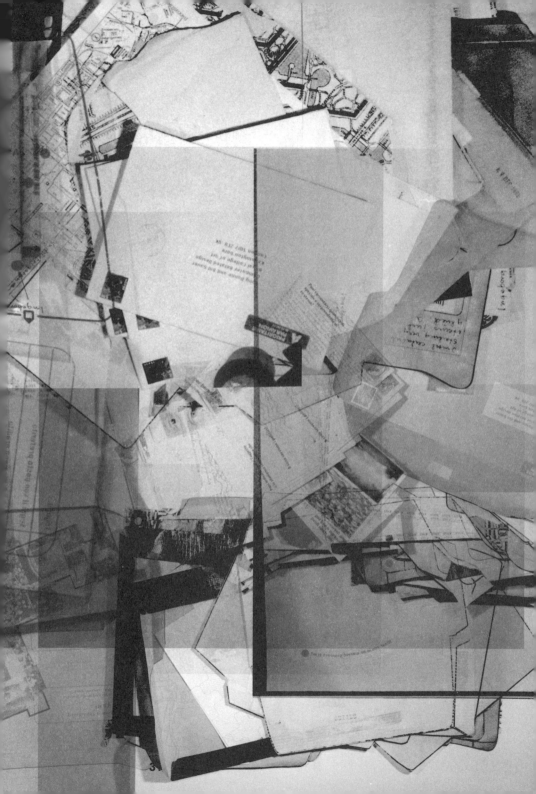

Che cosa non ti piace
di Peccioli?
È IL MIO PAESE
MI PIACE TUTTO

Pooi raccontarci qualcosa di
speciale e sorprendente di
te stesso?
SONO STATO A
2 FIGLI E 3 NIPOTI
SONO NATO PARIGIA
NO NELLA GUERRA
PASSATA, CONTRO
NAZZISTI E
FAGSISTI

Pooi indicarci qual'è l'oggetto
o lo strumento tecnologico che
preferisci?
IL TELEFONO

Che cosa non ti piace
di Peccioli?
È IL MIO PAESE
MI PIACE TUTTO

Pooi indicarci un consiglio che
si è rivelato importante nella
tua vita?

Pooi raccontarci qualcosa di
speciale e sorprendente di
te stesso?

Che cosa non ti piace
di Peccioli?
È IL MIO PAESE
MI PIACE TUTTO

Se potessi scegliere là radio
la tv, il computer, il video,
dove ti piacerebbe abitarci?
QUANDO SONO
IN CAMPAGNA
DA SOLO

Pooi indicarci ciò che è
si è rivelato importante nella
tua vita?
ESSERE
PERSEVERANTE.

32

33 WHAT IS YOUR FAVOURITE DEVICE? TELL US SOMETHING SPECIAL ABOUT YOURSELF.
     WHAT WOULD YOU LIKE TO HEAR ON THE RADIO FROM PECCIOLI? WHAT OR WHOM DO YOU MISS? (PECCIOLI)
34 TELL US ABOUT A PERSON WHO IS IMPORTANT TO YOU. TELL US ABOUT YOUR DAY. PLEASE TELL US ABOUT YOUR HOME.
     WHAT KIND OF PLACE IS THE INTERNET? WHAT KIND OF PLACE WOULD YOU LIKE IT TO BE? (MAJORSTUA)
35 TELL US SOMETHING SPECIAL ABOUT YOURSELF. WHAT IS YOUR FAVOURITE DEVICE? (BIJLMER)

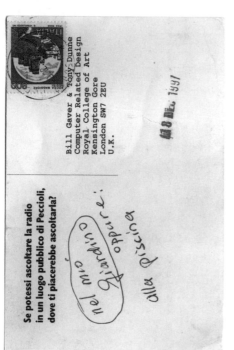

Puoi indicarci qual'e' l'oggetto o lo strumento tecnologico che preferisci?

il cannocchiale
per vedere il
Cielo e le stelle

Bill Gaver & Tony Dunne
Computer Related Design
Royal College of Art
Kensington Gore
London SW7 2EU
U.K.

8 DEC 1991

Se potessi ascoltare la radio in un luogo pubblico di Peccioli, dove ti piacerebbe ascoltarla?

nel mio Giardino
oppure:

alla Piscina

Bill Gaver & Tony Dunne
Computer Related Design
Royal College of Art
Kensington Gore
London SW7 2EU
U.K.

8 DEC 1991

Che cosa o chi ti manca di piu'?

I MEI PARENTI

Bill Gaver & Tony Dunne
Computer Related Design
Royal College of Art
Kensington Gore
London SW7 2EU
U.K.

17 NOV 1997
18 NOV 1997

Puoi raccontarci qualcosa di speciale e sorprendente di te stesso? La fortuna di essere riuscito a riunire che a Peccioli è have e con mezzi di fortuna, durante la ritirata dal fronte Russo, dove ci trovavo in Guerra quale artiliere appartenente all'A.R.M.I.R. (ARMATA ITALIANA in RUSSIA e di essere fortunatamente riuscito a fuggire, A PECCIOLI dalla cattura, con Quanti della truppa Tedeschi in ritirata che cercavano e riportavano in Germania sua gli uomini che riuscivano a fare abitazioni o i che rendevano nelle olotto propria essere.

Bill Gaver & Tony Dunne
Computer Related Design
Royal College of Art
Kensington Gore
London SW7 2EU
U.K.

11 NOV 1997

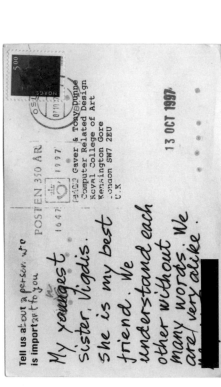

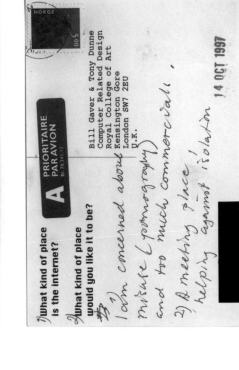

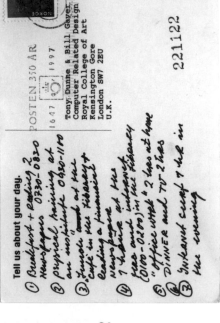

Please tell us about your home.

I have two homes, one in town (Oslo), and a very dear one on the coast by [Kragerø] — I love both of them, and they are different! My "country home" in Bamble or midway old things — I call it "my little museum". There I always have a piano and the same in town. I like to play a bit every day. I'm my "own home" I hire my many oysters, and paintings! And here I have my own piano! But I'll never be a "surfer".

Bill Gaver & Tony Dunne
Computer Related Design
Royal College of Art
Kensington Gore
London SW7 2EU
U.K.

POSTEN 350 ÅR   1997   14 OCT 1997

What kind of place is the internet?

What kind of place would you like it to be?

1) I am concerned about misuse (pornography) and too much commercial.

2) A meeting place! helping against isolation.

A PRIORITAIRE PARAVION

Bill Gaver & Tony Dunne
Computer Related Design
Royal College of Art
Kensington Gore
London SW7 2EU
U.K.

14 OCT 1997

Tell us about a person who is important to you

My youngest sister, Vigdis. She is my best friend. We understand each other without many words. We are very alike.

Bill Gaver & Tony Dunne
Computer Related Design
Royal College of Art
Kensington Gore
London SW7 2EU
U.K.

POSTEN 350 ÅR   1997   13 OCT 1997

Tell us about your day.

1) Breakfast + reading 2 newspapers 0730-0820
2) physical training at an institute 0850-1130
3) Lunch and at the café in the vicinity - reading a financial newspaper
4) 7 hours at the office and internet free... and interweb (0100-0200) in the vicinity
5) "office work" 2 hours at home
6) Dinner and TV 2 hrs
7) Internet exep 1 hr in the evening

221122

Tony, Dunne & Bill Gaver,
Computer Related Design
Royal College of Art
Kensington Gore
London SW7 2EU
U.K.

POSTEN 350 ÅR   1647   1997

34

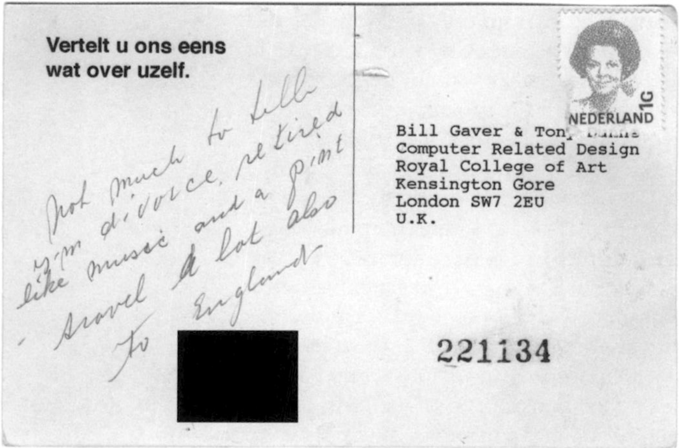
Vertelt u ons eens
wat over uzelf.

Not much to tell
I'm divorce, retired
like music and a print
- travel a lot also
to England

[redacted]

Bill Gaver & Tony Dunne
Computer Related Design
Royal College of Art
Kensington Gore
London SW7 2EU
U.K.

221134

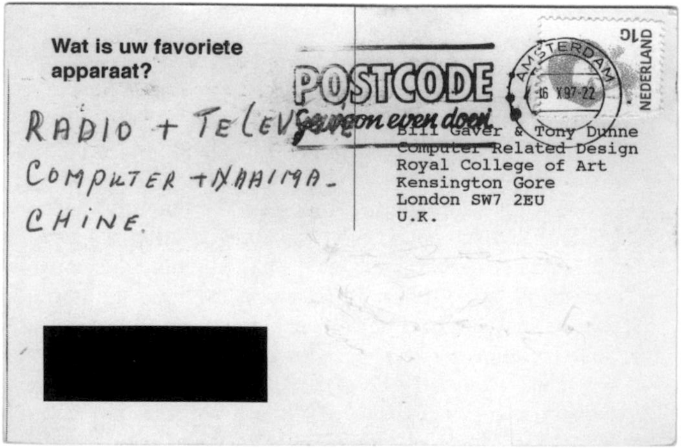
Wat is uw favoriete
apparaat?

RADIO + TELEV
COMPUTER + NAAIMA-
CHINE.

POSTCODE
Gewoon even doen

AMSTERDAM 16 X 97-22

NEDERLAND 1C

Bill Gaver & Tony Dunne
Computer Related Design
Royal College of Art
Kensington Gore
London SW7 2EU
U.K.

[redacted]

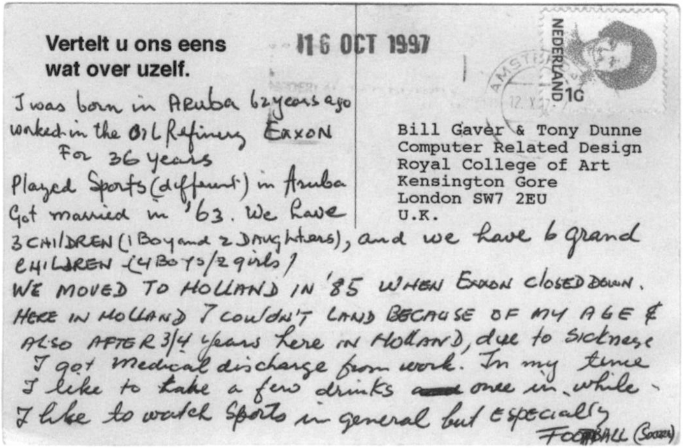
Vertelt u ons eens
wat over uzelf.

16 OCT 1997

I was born in Aruba 62 years ago
worked in the Oil Refinery EXXON
For 36 years
Played Sports (different) in Aruba
Got married in '63. We have
3 CHILDREN (1 Boy and 2 Daughters), and we have 6 grand
CHILDREN (4 BOYS/2 girls)
WE MOVED TO HOLLAND IN '85 WHEN EXXON CLOSED DOWN.
HERE IN HOLLAND I COULDN'T LAND BECAUSE OF MY AGE &
ALSO AFTER 3/4 years here in HOLLAND, due to sickness
I got medical discharge from work. In my time
I like to take a few drinks once in while.
I like to watch Sports in general but especially
FOOTBALL (Soccer)

NEDERLAND 1C

Bill Gaver & Tony Dunne
Computer Related Design
Royal College of Art
Kensington Gore
London SW7 2EU
U.K.

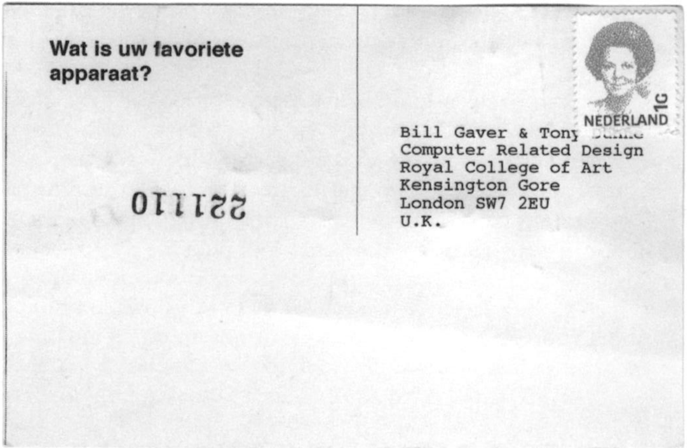
Wat is uw favoriete
apparaat?

221110

NEDERLAND 1C

Bill Gaver & Tony Dunne
Computer Related Design
Royal College of Art
Kensington Gore
London SW7 2EU
U.K.

PROJECTIVE-TESTS

The Rorschach inkblot test is probably the best known of the projective tests used by psychoanalysts. Created by folding paper onto which ink has been poured, the results are complex symmetrical shapes with no inherent representational meaning. Subjects are presented with these patterns, and asked to describe the images they see within them, like children finding animals or people in clouds.

The ways that people read meaning into these ambiguous shapes reveal clues about their inner lives. The content of their interpretations – whether the images they see tend to be threatening or benign, disturbing or beautiful – may reflect their hidden fears or desires, exposing their habitual orientation towards the world. The strategies they employ reveal still more. Do they employ the whole form, or just one part? Do they tend to focus on a particular part of the image, such as the centre or periphery? Which sorts of interpretations seem acceptable to them, and which are taboo? In their responses to this open, even nonsensical task, people reveal their approaches to everyday life, showing their preoccupations, their repressed urges and anxieties, and their orientation to authority.

The Rorschach test has been standardised both in presentation and scoring. The standard set of stimuli includes ten inkblots, of which the first five are monochrome, and the second five increasingly colourful. For each, the subject is asked 'what might this be?' and later prompted to clarify responses, so that a potentially open system is channelled and constrained. Interpretation, too, is often guided by codified scoring systems that allow responses to be measured along several dimensions. For instance, the role of more or less complex parts of the patterns might be recorded, or the degree to which colour is taken into account. This allows didactic constraints to be placed on therapists' interpretations, and responses to be compared across different situations.

Despite attempts to objectify the Rorschach test, however, it does not appear to live up to scientific ideals in terms of insensitivity to the attitudes of the people administering the test or those interpreting the results. Moreover, attempts to verify the interpretations that these techniques suggest have not been particularly successful. Difficulties in this regard are reflected by conflicts between approaches to systematising the test: for instance, some take the number of responses to a given stimulus to be relevant, while others limit the number of responses in the first place.

Many therapists acknowledge the subjectivity of tests like the Rorschach inkblots, and focus on the contents of the thoughts they elicit rather than on quantifiable aspects as originally recommended. From this point of view, although the Rorschach test is a kind of device for uncovering unconscious contents, it is not mechanical in its use: neither its administration nor its interpretation is automatic. Instead, the Rorschach test is a tool that can be employed with more or less sensitivity and skill, and the therapists who use it are themselves implicated in how they make sense of subjects' responses.

Another widely-used projective test is the Thematic Apperception Test. Developed in the 1940s, the test consists of about twenty images of people in evocative scenes suggesting but not defining key moments in unspecified narratives. Subjects are asked to give their first impressions about the stories suggested by the pictures, and as with the Rorschach test, their answers are taken as indicative of the contents of their unconscious. In dealing with scenes from everyday life, the Thematic Apperception Test may trigger stories closer to the realities of subjects' day-to-day struggles, rather than the more abstract themes evoked by the Rorschach inkblots.

Whereas Rorschach inkblots are selected from patterns created by chance, the pictures used for the Thematic Apperception Test were consciously designed or chosen. Thus they reveal both the culture and style of their time, as well as the implicit hypotheses and concerns of their designers. On the one hand, this has meant that the original stimuli have been deemed inappropriate for certain cultures (e.g. a special set exists for use in China). On the other hand, using the original cards sets up a complicated set of suggestions and counter-suggestions involving the original designer, the therapist and the subject.

Projective tests may thus be seen as varying in the degree to which they allow or prevent a personal dialogue to emerge between the subject and the therapist. Chance stimuli like the inkblots protect both the original designer and the therapist from inadvertently revealing themselves – although one must not overlook the fact that the standard set of ten were presumably selected from a much larger set of possibilities. Designed stimuli, such as the Thematic Apperception Test, may reveal the culture and concerns of the original developer, but shield the therapist, especially when they are standardised. Still other techniques, however, such as sentence-completion tasks or word-association tests, may reveal the therapists' own conflicts or assumptions about the subject.

Within the psychoanalytic framework, it is considered crucial to hide the therapist's own beliefs and concerns. This not only allows attention to be focused solely on the subjects' situation, but more importantly, by remaining unknown, the therapist becomes a blank canvas for the 'transference' relationship that has classically been considered a fundamental tool for analysis. Nonetheless, in moving away from chance towards designed stimuli, and relaxing demands for objectivity, standardisation, and replicability, projective tests might become springboards for communication rather than diagnosis, leading to a mutual endeavour aimed at understanding and reconsidering one's orientation towards life.

38-39 WHAT'S YOUR FAVOURITE PLACE? WHERE WOULD YOU LIKE TO GO BUT CAN'T?... (PECCIOLI)
40-41 WHERE HAVE YOU BEEN IN THE WORLD? (ALL SITES) WHERE HAVE YOU VISITED ON THE WEB? (MAJORSTUA)
42-43 WHERE DO YOU FEEL AFRAID, CAUTIOUS, OR SAFE? (THE BIJLMER)
44-45 IF THE BIJLMER WERE A BODY... (THE BIJLMER)
46-47 DRAW A MAP FROM YOUR HOME TO THE LIBRARY. (MAJORSTUA)

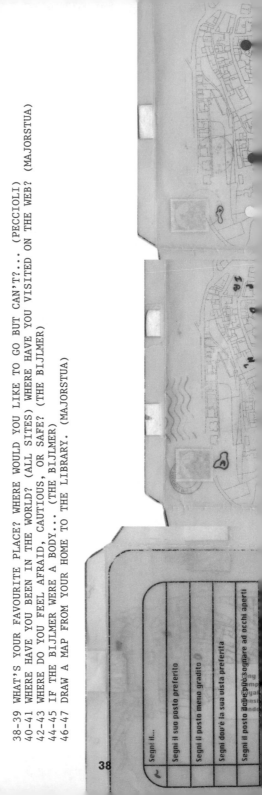

Segni il...

Segni il suo posto preferito

Segni il posto meno gradito

Segni dov'è la sua vista preferita

Segni il posto dove può sognare ad occhi aperti

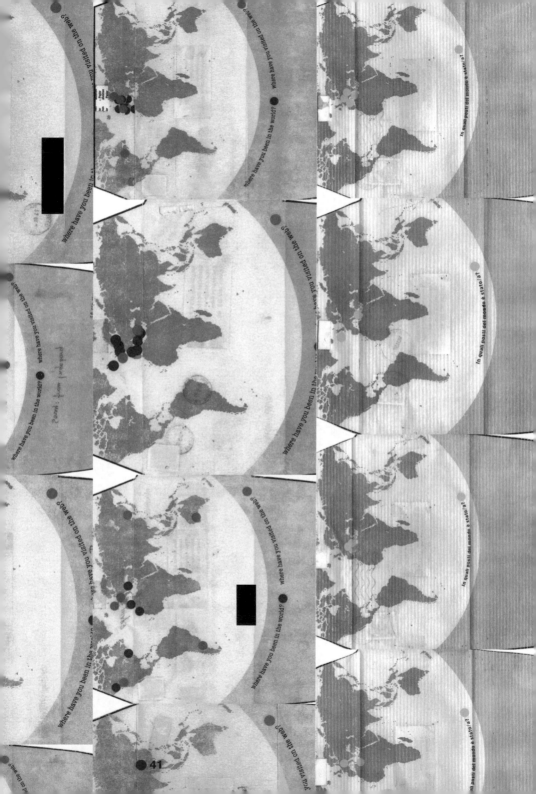

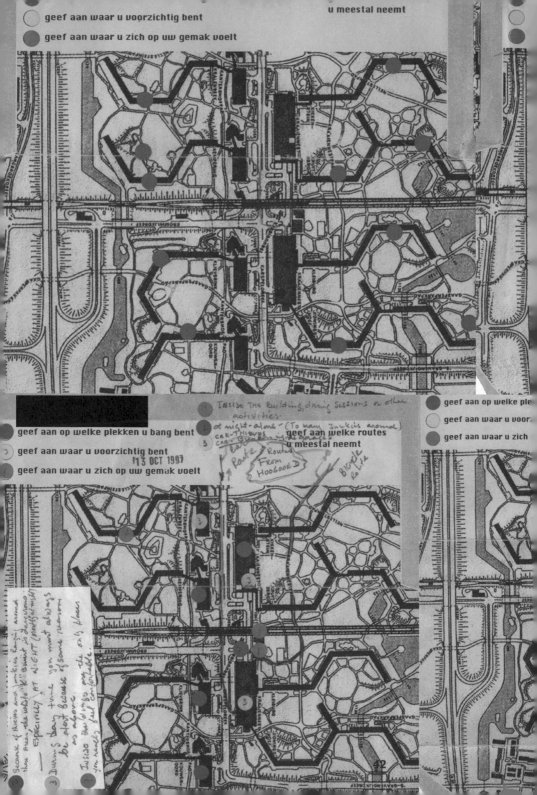

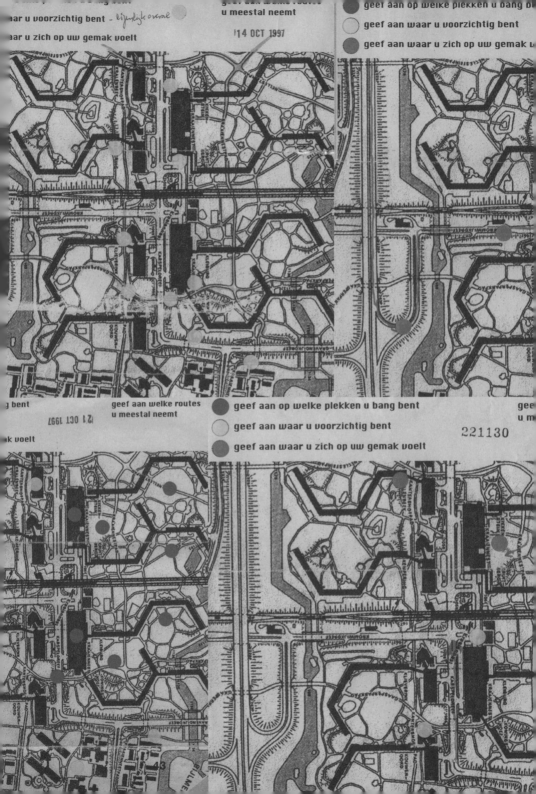

geef aan op welke plekken u bang b[...]

geef aan waar u voorzichtig bent

geef aan waar u zich op uw gemak [...]

aar u voorzichtig bent - *bijzonder overal*

aar u zich op uw gemak voelt

geef aan welke routes
u meestal neemt

14 OCT 1997

g bent

k voelt

geef aan welke routes
u meestal neemt

21 OCT 1997

geef aan op welke plekken u bang bent

geef aan waar u voorzichtig bent

geef aan waar u zich op uw gemak voelt

221130

gee[...]

u m[...]

43

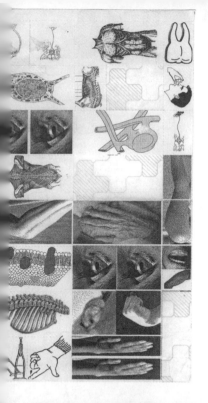

UIT DIT KAARTJE KAN IK NIETS WIJS WORDEN

Stelt u zich eens voor dat de Bijlmer
een lichaam was...   2 0 OCT 1997

SORRY!

45

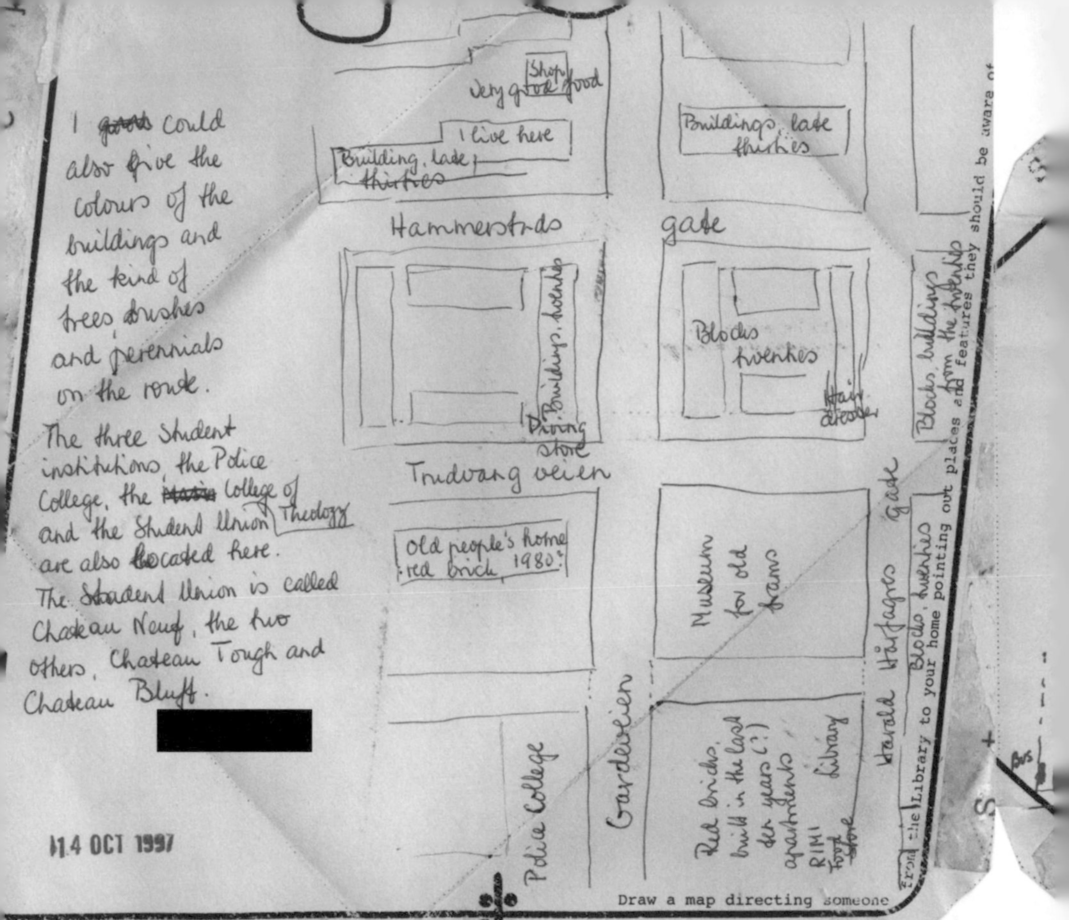

I could also give the colours of the buildings and the kind of trees, bushes and perennials on the route.

The three student institutions, the Police College, the College of Theology and the Student Union are also located here.
The Student Union is called Chateau Neuf, the two others, Chateau Tough and Chateau Bluff.

14 OCT 1997

Map (top):
- very good food — Shop
- I live here
- Building, late thirties
- Buildings, late thirties
- Hammersteds gate
- Building, hotel(?)
- Blocks twenties
- Hair dresser
- Blocks, buildings
- Diving store
- Trudvang veien
- Old people's home red brick, 1980's
- Museum for old trams
- Gardeveien
- Red bricks, built in the last ten years (?) apartments
- RIMI food store
- Library
- Police College
- Harald Hårfagres gate
- From the Library to your home pointing out places and features they should be aware of 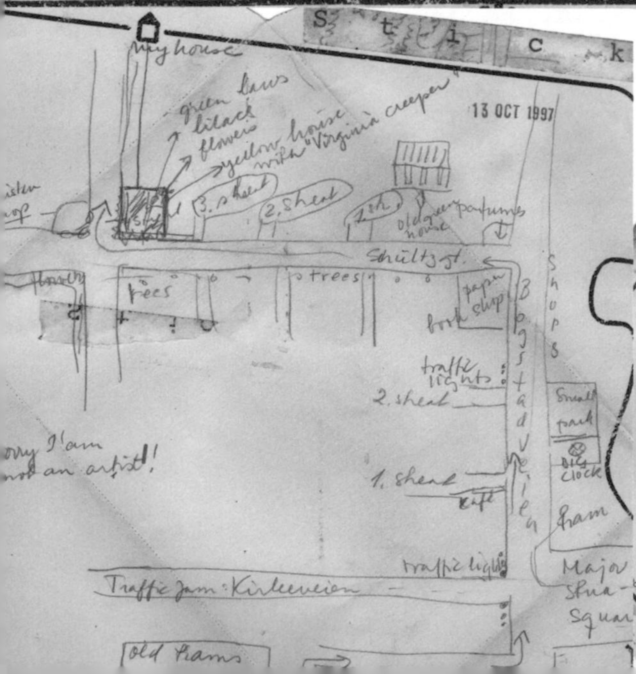
- Draw a map directing someone
- BUS

Map (bottom left):
- my house
- green lawn, lilack flowers
- yellow house with Virginia creeper
- 13 OCT 1997
- 3. sheet
- 2. sheet
- old ... perfumes house
- Schultz st.
- trees / trees
- book shop
- paper shop
- traffic lights
- 2. sheet
- Shops
- Small park
- Big clock
- 1. sheet
- tram
- Major Stua Square
- traffic lights
- Traffic Jam: Kirkeveien
- old trams
- Bogstadveien
- Sorry I am not an artist!

Map (bottom right):
I would take a circuit pointing out the Mission Church, the EIDRE SENTER, the Academy of music (with many concerts) the MAJORSTUEN STASJON, the Vine monoply, the chemist's shop, BANK, POST, 2 good restaurants

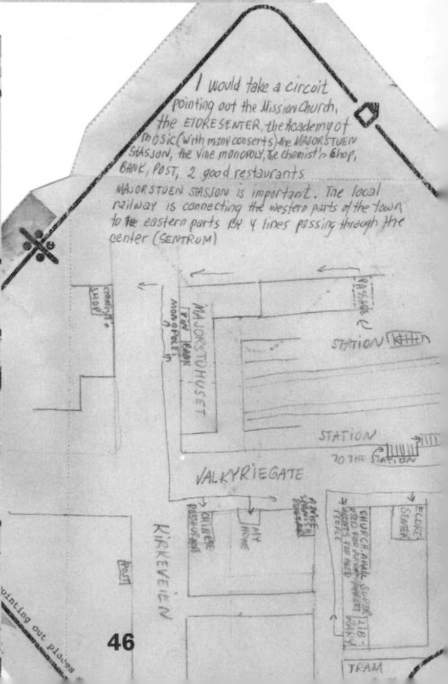

MAJORSTUEN STASJON is important. The local railway is connecting the western parts of the town to the eastern parts by 4 lines passing through the center (SENTRUM)

- MAJORSTUHUSET
- STATION
- STATION TO THE
- VALKYRIEGATE
- KIRKEVEIEN
- TRAM
- pointing out places

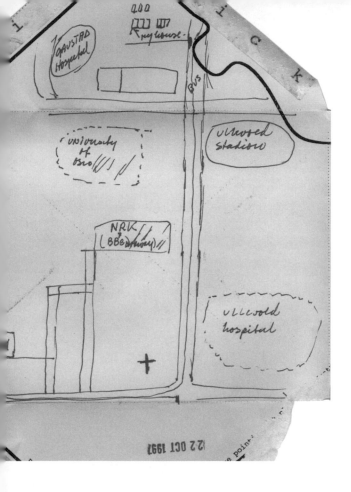

47

TAKE A PICTURE OF SOMETHING BEAUTIFUL
TAKE A PICTURE OF YOUR FAVOURITE DEVICE
TAKE A PICTURE OF SOMETHING BORING
TAKE A PICTURE OUT YOUR WINDOW
TAKE A PICTURE OF WHAT YOU WILL WEAR TODAY...

51,53,59,62,63,66,71 (PECCIOLI)
49,55,64,67,68,69,70,72 (OSLO)
50,52,54,56,57,58,60,61,65 (THE BIJLMER)

Proposals

The second main phase of the project involved generating a wide range of proposals for each of the three sites. Using the returns from the Cultural Probes, as well as photographs, anecdotes, and souvenirs from our visits, we imagined a wide variety of systems that we might develop and recorded our ideas for discussion with our partners and the groups of older people at each of the sites.

The proposals were developed in three stages lasting about nine months in total. In the first stage, we simply gathered design ideas in the form of rough sketches, collages, and phrases, and collected them into a scrapbook. Little effort was wasted in developing the ideas beyond reminders or suggestions to ourselves, so the scrapbook was difficult for outsiders to understand without our interpretation. Nonetheless, it provided a crucial starting point for discussing our interests and inclinations with our partners.

During the second stage, we began to filter the ideas, developing some and discarding others, until proposals for each of the three sites developed distinct identities. Capturing these in a more structured workbook, we used a variety of imagery to create fragmented narratives for the systems we were proposing, while using descriptive text to provide a framework and organisation for the ideas. These workbooks were presented to the older people in each of the three sites during visits, to encourage them to imagine the ideas and to elicit their feedback and ideas.

Discussing the workbook with the older people and our partners allowed us to crystallise the design proposals for each site in the third and final stage. What had started as loose constellations of ideas six months earlier cohered as integrated systems, the result of having been inhabited by our imaginations for so long. This time we presented them in the form of a multimedia presentation. Separate screens described each community to set the context for our proposals, presented animated diagrams of the systems we suggested, and offered a 'catalogue of parts' indicating the kinds of physical artefacts that might comprise the systems. The presentation was the culmination of this phase: though each of the proposals developed further as we developed them for testing, their essential character was formed at this time.

In presenting this phase of the project, we allow work from the first two stages to flow together, to paint a picture of the ideas we considered and the systems we finally proposed. This section of the book is divided only by the three sites: we are intertwining the sketches, collages, and diagrams to create an impression of how our initial ideas grew into fully formed concept proposals.

These are summarised at the end using images taken from the final CD ROM presentation.

PECCIOLI RADIOSCAPE / From the first visit to Peccioli, our thoughts were drawn towards using radio as a way of overlaying and extending the village and its rural surroundings. Perhaps the wiring run casually over the peeling stucco walls, television antennae pointing uniformly towards unseen targets, and panoramic views of the countryside glimpsed through narrow streets and passageways combined to persuade us that an uncomplicated technology would be most appropriate for the site. Certainly the older inhabitants' evident sociability, long chats in local cafes, and their appreciation for the town's pastoral setting convinced us to enhance their existing pleasures, rather than to solve problems we couldn't find.

The returns from the Probes encouraged these notions. Photographs showed the older people gathered in the streets or in their homes. Maps marked many places they enjoyed, and only one – the cemetery – which made them wary. Cards complained of only one problem with Peccioli: the construction of the local cinema was not yet complete.

Some of our proposals explored how radio could be used to amplify the sociability of this close-knit community. We imagined that older people might borrow two-way radios from the local elder centre and use them to communicate with their friends or family members. This developed into a proposal for transmitter-receiver units, each devoted to a single wavelength. Separating the transmitter from the receiver would allow people to exchange them, setting up flexible communication networks. If two people exchanged their transmitters, for instance, they could talk with one another. If other people wanted to join in, they could pass along their transmitters, forming loops and chains of communication. If a transmitter was left somewhere – in a cafe, for instance, or a field – then everybody in the chain could hear the noises it picked up.

Other ideas built on the notion of transmitting sounds from the countryside into the village. Transmitters with built-in microphones might be planted beside streams or in the woods, allowing people to tune into birds or splashing water. Some might have attached wind vanes, so they would pick up sounds from different directions depending on which way the wind was blowing. Still others might be worn by cows or other animals, sending back the ambience of their journeys. We hoped, in this way, to build up a rich pastoral soundscape, allowing the older people to enjoy the surrounding countryside from their homes in the village.

Tourists, too, might engage with Peccioli's radioscape. Roadside lay-bys could be equipped with low-power transmitters, playing sounds picked up from a visible landmark, or stories and songs collected by the older villagers. Perhaps an overall soundscape would be broadcast, with new layers being added as the village grew nearer by low-power transmitters broadcasting on the same frequency. Tourists might even partake in the social radioscape, using devices found in guest houses or hotels in the area to share an auditory visit with older people in the village.

At heart, the ideas envisioned an alternative to commercial radio which, with its generic music, advertising and news, tends to discount rather than appreciate regional differences. The combination of social, pastoral, and touristic radioscapes suggest new possibilities for this traditional medium. By promoting casual conversation, linking strangers with local inhabitants and allowing remote access to the countryside, the system offered a new dimension to Peccioli's existing community (pp. 84-95).

MAJORSTUA DIGITAL BOUDOIR / The Majorstua, in Oslo, is an affluent, even bourgeois community. During our visits, we encountered shops specialising in luxury items and handcrafted gifts, expensive restaurants, and clean streets. A pleasant district, there was no 'edge' to it, apart from a few drunks cadging cigarettes on a street corner near the train station.

The older inhabitants, for the most part, were well educated and comfortable in retirement. The group we worked with met in the local library to learn how to use the Internet, an activity they shared with local school children. They were enthusiastic about accessing information from around the world, but less interested in local issues. The local government was keen to collaborate with the project to expand their website, which was seldom used despite offering updates on policies and the ability for citizens to interact with politicians.

Our ideas centred around ways to encourage the older people to engage more with issues and events within the Majorstua. Unlike the other two sites, there was little feeling of a community identity in the area; instead, the district merged with other areas of Oslo, and people didn't seem to interact as a local community. Our proposals were, to some degree, meant to provoke the older locals to become more present in their community – not only in the sense of being more noticeable, but also in the sense of being more aware of the society immediately surrounding them.

Our first ideas centred around exaggerating the privileged position of the older Internet users in the library. We imagined transforming the functional library room in which they met into a 'Digital Boudoir'. Filled with luxurious furniture-technology hybrids, the boudoir would allow the group to lounge in comfort while exploring the diverse pleasures of the World Wide Web.

The notion of a boudoir expanded to include its function as a place for discussion. We imagined the elders would become the centre of a community-wide conversation about local issues from their comfortable surroundings. Other locals might encounter various manifestations of this debate. Large billboards could display controversial issues, to which passers-by might respond in some way. Viewfinders like those found at tourist viewpoints might be installed, designed to overlay social and political information on the city like an interactive psychogeographical map. Statements about local topics might be printed on tram tickets and shopping receipts to spur new conversations.

Over time, these ideas gelled into an integrated system: special furniture in the library would allow the elders to sort through information on the Web or provided by the local politicians, pulling out topics the group found interesting. Other furniture would mediate their discussions about the issues, allowing them to distil them into relevant questions for public release.

Questions formulated by the group would be relayed to the local tram station, where they would wait to be transmitted to passing trams. Moving from tram to tram, the questions would disperse throughout the local area. They might appear on displays mounted in the trams, at tram stops, or in local cafes, with people able to reply by pressing 'yes' and 'no' buttons on associated devices. Automated Teller Machines (ATMs) in the area might display the questions, or local telephone booths might ring occasionally and pose them to anybody who answered. When a quota of answers had been reached, each question would return to the library so that the elders could report the results to the community and local politicians. Unpopular questions which didn't meet their quota, meanwhile, would be sent to isolated areas to languish.

The Digital Boudoir proposal cast the older people of the Majorstua as curators, or perhaps hosts, of the local political culture. We wanted to encourage them to express their views publicly, and moreover to listen to people's answers. This proposal, more than the others, sought to emphasise the responsibilities as well as privileges of being present in a local community (pp. 98-105).

BIJLMER PROJECTED REALITIES / The Bijlmer was the most complex of the three communities. Warned about the dangers of the area, there were times when we were distinctly uneasy when we visited. But we also found ourselves strolling on sunny paths between meadows and canals as we made our way through the district, or exploring the diverse products and produce for sale in the local market beneath the roadway.

The probe returns and our conversations with the older people reinforced these impressions of contradiction. We heard many stories of the security problems of the area: the seeming reluctance of police to respond to calls from the Bijlmer, the threats offered by junkies and burglars, continuing racism and neglect. Yet equally many discussions focused on local attractions: the richness of the cultural mix, the opportunities for social gatherings, the custom of bringing caged birds outdoors to sing in the sunshine. Overall, we sensed a kind of defiant pride in the area. While plagued with the typical problems of urban housing projects, people are proud to live in the Bijlmer and there is a strong sense of community about it.

Nonetheless, the widespread perception that fear is the Bijlmer's defining feature overwhelmed our initial design discussions. We found ourselves speculating about laser pointers distributed to the older inhabitants so they could draw attention to threatening characters, or the possibility of projecting comments and warnings on the outside of miscreants' flats. These culminated in proposals – sparked by a chance photograph – for cages to be situated in the area, into which the older inhabitants could lock themselves to enjoy the outdoors without fear. Neither entirely serious nor merely tasteless jokes, such ideas were a way of working through our initial preoccupation with safety, and of dramatising the problems of designing with an obsession for security – highlighting the danger that electronic systems might themselves become cages for older people.

Our ideas turned towards ways to promote communication within and to the outskirts of the Bijlmer. We thought about projecting homemade soap operas onto billboards along the roads surrounding the area, offering a glimpse into the mundane realities of the area, or perhaps satirically exaggerating stereotypes about it. We suggested that security cameras might be linked together to create a network of 'virtual neighbourhoods' promoting new encounters and the possibility of extended neighbourhood watch schemes. We proposed 'vent crawlers', robots that could travel the ventilation ducts, recording and broadcasting fragments of conversations to allow people to share the different cultural lifestyles of their neighbours, or a 'mains radio system' that would broadcast voice and data over the existing power network within the buildings. Finally, we thought of ways to share people's knowledge of the area's emotional topography, perhaps using pagers to indicate where they felt safe or anxious, for publication on electronic or paper maps.

In meeting the group of older residents to discuss our ideas, we found they recognised even the most unusual as reflecting issues in the area. They hesitated over some of the proposals –

the vent crawlers, they thought, might help burglars discover when flats were unoccupied, and the psychogeographic maps would only be useful for visitors. But they rejected none of the ideas outright, and saw sense in them all. In particular, they responded enthusiastically to our suggestions that a system could help inhabitants counter the bad reputation of the Bijlmer.

Focusing the concepts, we started to integrate the ideas into a system that would allow people's beliefs and attitudes to project from their individual homes, through local neighbourhoods, to the outskirts of the Bijlmer. Using special 'scanning furniture', the elders would collect images and slogans about their lives in the Bijlmer. These would be accessible via a mains radio system to local residents, who would indicate their attitudes and dispositions by choosing images or slogans to display. Amalgamating choices over sections of the housing blocks would give a local mood that could be reflected by 'slogan furniture' in the neighbourhood. Slogans, finally, would be collected to determine images shown on large 'image boards' near the commuter roads and railways surrounding the Bijlmer.

The Projected Realities proposal, in essence, was to create a distributed analogue network for representing the Bijlmer. Elements of expression would spread from individuals, through neighbourhoods, ultimately to form a kind of public face for the area. The older residents would be most influential in this process, by choosing the images and slogans to be used. But no one person or group would have ultimate control over the end result. Instead, each person's contribution would be distributed over the entire network, with the end result – the images representing the Bijlmer to outsiders – emerging from the layers behind it (pp. 108-117).

NARRATIVE

Without some notion of cause and effect, a story is merely a random set of unconnected events. Temporal flow might be established amongst them (first this happened, then that, then this...), but narrative only emerges when episodes are connected by necessity – when a building falls because there has been an earthquake, for instance, or because a bomb has been set off. In the absence of a causal chain, there is no story to be told, no narrative trajectory to follow.

Social causality underlies the most compelling narratives, because in people's choices other possibilities are implied. Buildings have no alternative but to collapse if a blast is strong enough. People, in contrast, do have the choice whether or not to set off a bomb. In these momentary crossroads on the causal path, as Aristotle pointed out, meanings and characters are defined. The bomber might be a psychopath or a demolitions expert; his or her character is revealed by the choice to bomb or not. But his or her choice may equally be the result of a causal chain, raising the tension between free will and determinism.

In recounting a narrative, every scene might in principle take part in a causal chain, impelled by preceding events and partially determining future ones. In practice, scenes may be used to establish genre, atmosphere, or locale, helping the audience to interpret events without themselves taking a causal role in the sequence. In addition, links in the causal chain are often omitted and left for the audience to infer. For this reason, it is crucial to distinguish the plot – events that are actually portrayed – from the story – the entire causal chain, when considering how a narrative is portrayed.

Audiences are extremely sophisticated in using cues about genre, character type, and typical event sequences to understand the causal trajectory that forms a story. For this reason, it is difficult to introduce new kinds of stories that contradict familiar genres. Existing types are combined, extended, and confounded in small ways, but they are seldom either abandoned or introduced.

Experimental film, for instance by the Surrealists, did attempt to break with traditional forms of narrative. In part an attempt to understand the medium of film in its own right, in part to explore and reflect their ideas about subjective mental life, they deliberately set out to disrupt conventional notions of cause and effect in narratives. Some, for example, explored sensual mappings between imagery and sound, producing multimedia versions of abstract paintings. Others allowed plot and story to become one, questioning causality in mundane life. Still others introduced fantastic forms of logic or imagery, based on dreams, in order to subvert rational notions of causality in mental life. These experiments disrupted people's ability to make sense of events, with liberating or disturbing effects.

Even the most radical of these narrative forms, however, have been appropriated into the mainstream. Dream sequences, hallucinatory visions, abstract sequences of images and sound, all are familiar techniques to audiences of movies, television shows, even advertisements. Such techniques are made safe by compartmentalising them, forming new links in an overall causal chain. But the potential power of experimental narratives should not be discounted. In serving to momentarily disrupt the flow of cause and effect, they may open a space in which the audience can find glimpses of causal possibilities beyond the ordinary.

While some film-makers have sought to escape causal narrative, many 'still-image' artists have sought to exploit it in their work. From paintings joining multiple scenes on a unified backdrop to comic strips made up of several distinct panels, from the photomontage techniques of Dada and the Surrealists to the Futurists' attempts to capture motion, a myriad of techniques have been developed for imbuing a still image with a sense of causal flow.

John Baldessari's photographic constructions of the 1980s, for instance, juxtapose a variety of images to create ambiguous narrative possibilities. In some, visual elements serve as stage settings or props: a lurid print of a sunset is placed over a diagram of an earthquake; beneath is a photograph of three billiard balls in a line. Other constructions show populated scenes: three men, one with a gun, crouch behind suitcases and blank canvases, while below a businessman leans to kiss a woman in bed – all the faces concealed by coloured dots. These images resonate with one another to create tantalising stories, with clues for possible genres colliding and tugging against one another.

Cindy Sherman's Untitled Film Stills series, in contrast, resembles key frames from mainstream movies. Containing many of the visual indications of genre, such as costume, lighting and set, the scenes themselves seem to be selected from moments between key episodes – just before or after a defining event. Cueing involuntary expectations and associations based on viewers' familiarity with movies, they evoke fragmentary stories and dramatic situations.

One of the concerns of Sherman's work is to criticise the commodification of women into a finite set of narrative genres by exposing the absurdity of recreating a woman's story from a single image. But our impulse to do so, our implicit belief that such is possible and appropriate, drives the work. What Sherman and similar narrative artists show is that plot can be distilled to a single image and the audience impelled to recreate an entire story.

you are now entering a pastoral radioscape

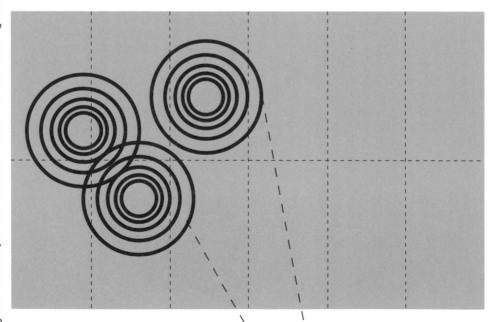

3 folk songs, 1 story and some advice...

the story about the winter of ...

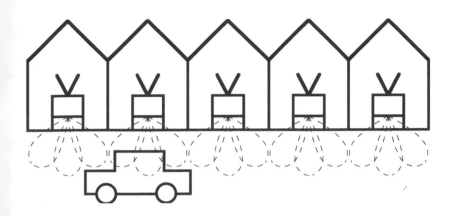

bed & breakfast & soundscapes

leaky houses and media tourism

strolling through the radioscape you may come across elements of interest

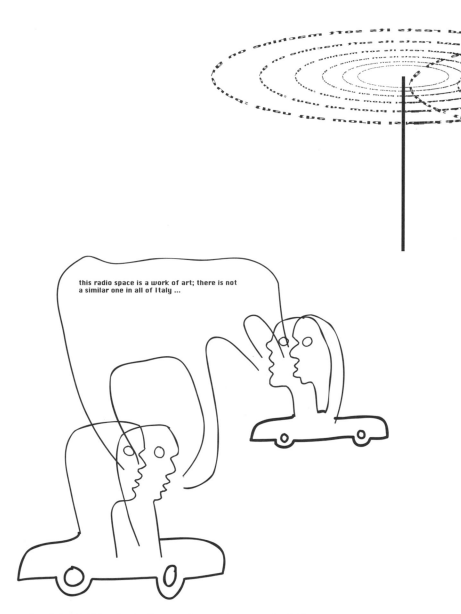

87

cattle and wildlife tagged with location transmitters

when a calf is born in Peccioli, it is fitted with a solar collar

the slow, grazing movements of the animals create therapeutic and calming images on the location receivers

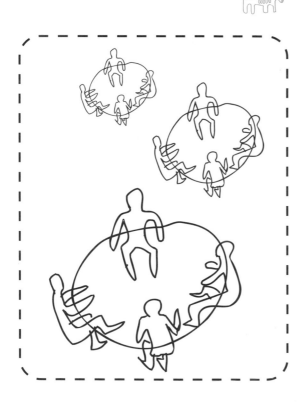

having been lost for days, everyone's favourite radio sheep was broadcasting again...

GOSSIP FROM THE NEIGHBOURING VILLAGE IS TRANSMITTED TO PECCIOLI

arcadian radioscapes and tourism

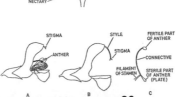

an unregulated market of radioscapes; trading, stealing, jamming...

listening to growing plants

italian catchflower

sound feeder

container-amplifier-radial-helipod-diffuser

sound clipper-feeder-extension

PETAL
STAMEN
CARPEL
SEPAL
NECTARY

STIGMA
ANTHER
STYLE
STIGMA
FERTILE PART OF ANTHER
CONNECTIVE
FILAMENT OF STAMEN
STERILE PART OF ANTHER (PLATE)

A   B   C

90

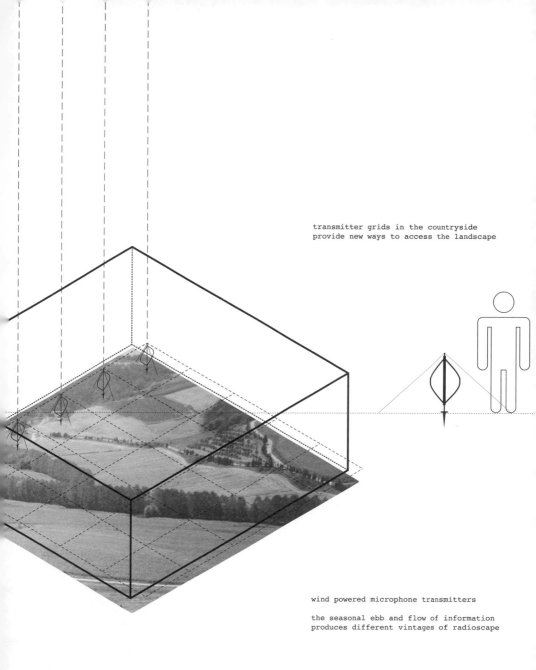

transmitter grids in the countryside
provide new ways to access the landscape

wind powered microphone transmitters

the seasonal ebb and flow of information
produces different vintages of radioscape

over time, the radios
disperse across the
Tuscany landscape...

1 month

2 months

3 months

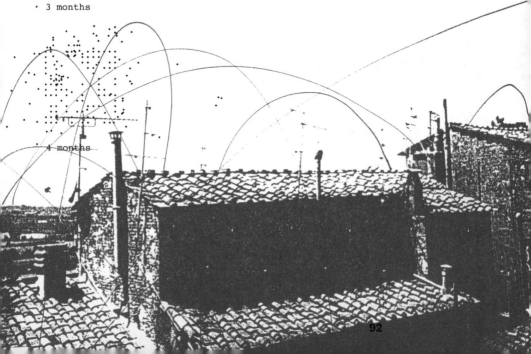

4 months

sounds of the landscape

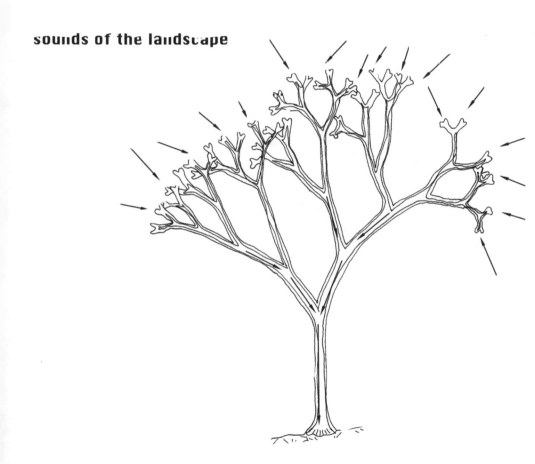

section through 'tree of peccioli' [the antenna]

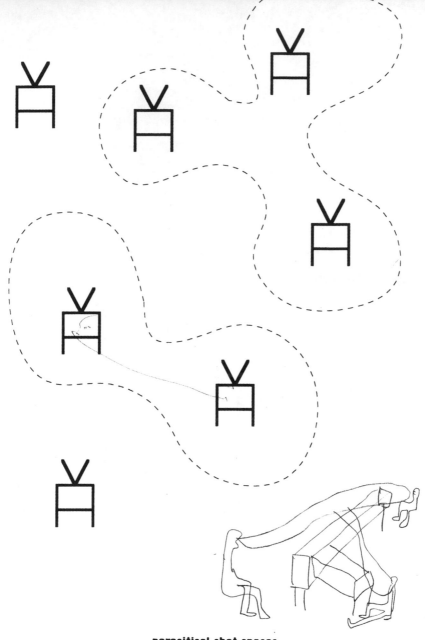

parasitical chat spaces

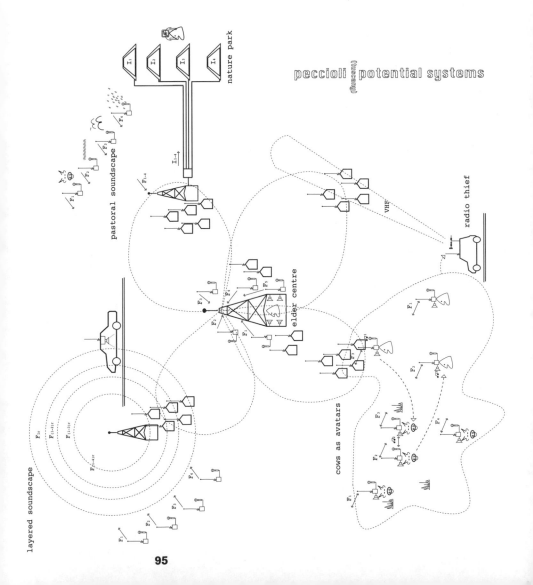

peccioli potential systems

nature park

pastoral soundscape

layered soundscape

elder centre

cows as avatars

radio thief

95

RADIO --------

Guglielmo Marconi is often credited as the inventor of radio, largely because he was first to patent key ideas and to develop their business potential. But wireless communication dates back at least to Faraday's discovery of electromagnetic induction in 1831: passing a wire through a magnetic field causes an electric current; conversely, passing current through a wire causes a magnetic field to form. Maxwell's 1864 equations describing electromagnetic waves predicted that this interdependence of electric and magnetic forces does not require a wire, or indeed any medium. The waves produced by running a current through one wire can induce a current in another, completely separate wire – the basis for radio, TV, and indeed most wireless communications.

A number of engineers, inventors, and scientists experimented with wireless transmission of electricity, including Mahlon Loomis in 1865 and Alexander Graham Bell in 1882, but it was Heinrich Hertz, in 1887, who first recognised this phenomenon as a manifestation of Maxwell's electromagnetic radiation. Hertz's research, and that of others, provided the foundation for Marconi's business developing, promoting, and manufacturing wireless equipment.

Wireless boomed in the early 1900s, despite the fact that it depended on spark transmitters to send short pulses of energy and was thus suited only for wireless telegraphy. Finding practical application in connecting ships to shore, it quickly developed an avid following among amateurs interested in experimenting with this new form of communication. The development of equipment capable of producing continuous waves modulated by a microphone allowed speech and music to be transmitted, contributing to the increase in radio's popularity. A growing number of enthusiasts bought or built receivers known as 'cats whiskers', named for the fine wire that had to be manoeuvred against a crystal to tune the set. The excitement was such that despite a lack of profits, U.S. radio companies sold stock at vastly inflated prices in the 1910s – a boom that ended when several companies were prosecuted for fraudulent practices and patent infringements.

As amateurs' experiments in transmitting speech, and particularly music, became more popular, the prevailing uses of radio as a means of one-to-one communication came under increasing pressure. Although the ability to tune radios to particular frequencies had been developing since the mid-1890s, tests and informal communications often interfered with naval communications and musical transmissions. The former incensed the government; the latter the public. Then, in 1912, came the Titanic disaster. Not only did nearby ships have their receivers turned off, missing the Titanic's distress signals, but amateur broadcasts confused and misled efforts on the mainland to monitor the situation.

By the end of 1912, legislation was passed in the U.S. restricting amateur stations to a limited frequency range. World War I saw even greater restrictions, with receivers as well as transmitters being forbidden both in the U.K. and the U.S. out of fear that information might be passed to the enemy inadvertently or due to deliberate spying. By the end of the war, the regulation of radio seemed inevitable.

The transition of wireless from a communications to a broadcast medium was similarly the result of wartime restrictions, the use of radio to entertain troops, and the growth of wireless companies. Although amateur transmitters still operated, they came under escalating regulations confining them to frequencies considered useless. The remaining spectrum was quickly purchased by a number of large companies, such as the BBC, formed out of military radio services to broadcast news, entertainment, and advertisements to home audiences.

Receivers were domesticated to become commodities for the home. The raw technology was hidden by wooden and fabric surrounds to resemble furniture, and even incorporated into lamps, chairs, and cabinets. Only in the 1930s did radios emerge from their camouflage, when the development of Bakelite allowed new forms to be developed, giving rise to the genre of high-technology appliances – a return to the era of unabashed technology, but neutered to witness rather than participate in the newly civilised medium.

Although broadcasting corporations and fears of electromagnetic anarchy largely pushed amateur radio operators out of the spectrum, pockets of autonomous use remain. The popularity of Citizens' Band (CB) radio soared in the U.S. during the 1970s, reinvigorating wireless as a two-way communications medium. Thousands of amateurs transmitted and received messages free from commercial or governmental mediation. Though clearly disassociated with any radical political movement, CB was nonetheless often used for subversive ends, from circumventing authority to virtual sex-play. Romanticised in popular music and movies, the phenomenon reflected a kind of grass-roots liberation movement mediated by, and perhaps existing only in, the space of the radio spectrum.

Meanwhile, underground broadcasts from the 1960s to the present often pursue a more explicitly political agenda. Stations in Italy, Japan, the U.S., and the Netherlands broadcast a variety of political views, surrealist and anarchist sound experiments, and anti-establishment music as an alternative to tightly controlled commercial and state media. Sometimes exploiting regulations allowing low-power transmissions, sometimes blatantly defying the law, such stations spread a variety of counter-cultural views to a wide audience. Most stations abandoned any overt political agenda in the 1970s and 1980s, but waves of new underground broadcasts continue to emerge and vanish as authorities relax and tighten control.

Rather than contest radio's cultural uses, some people choose to forgo all human civilisation in the spectrum. Travelling to remote deserts and mountains, they monitor and record clicks, tones, and textures caused by high-level atmospheric phenomena. Easily disrupted by commercial broadcasts, aircraft communications, even the hum of distant high-voltage lines, recordings are captured with painstaking care using specialised equipment, to be sold and bartered by hobbyists and specialist distributors. To listen to these sounds is to experience radio as a wilderness. In their delicate and elusive beauty, they remind us how recently, and how thoroughly, the electromagnetic spectrum has been settled, zoned, and commercialised.

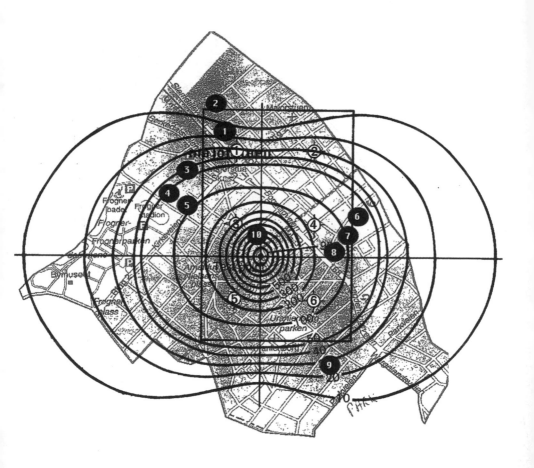

the library is the centre of a field of interaction that spreads throughout the Majorstua

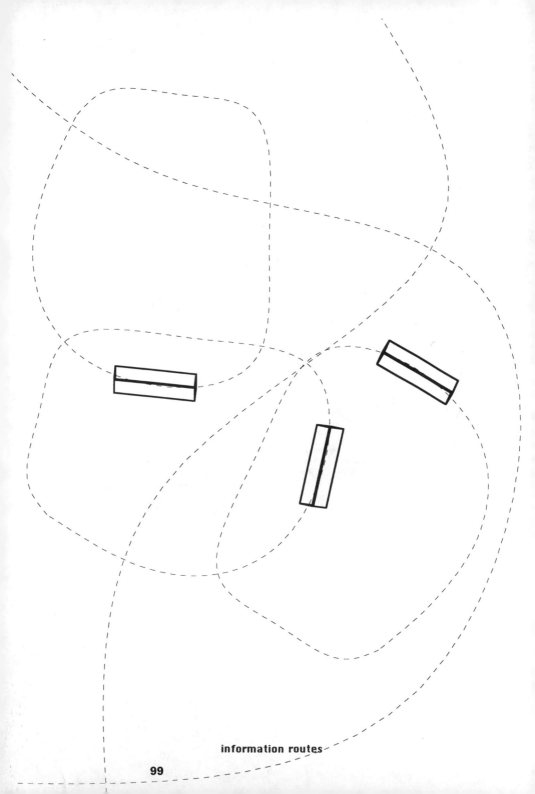

information routes

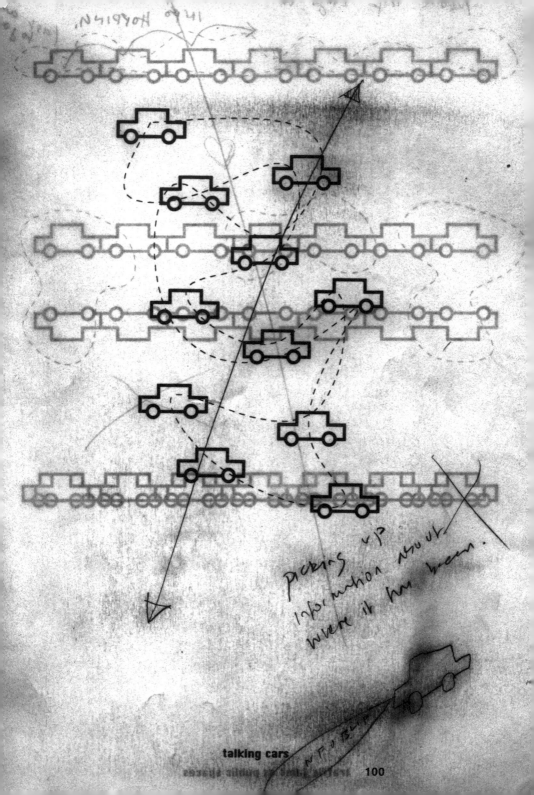

INFO HOARDIN'

picking up
information about
where it has been.

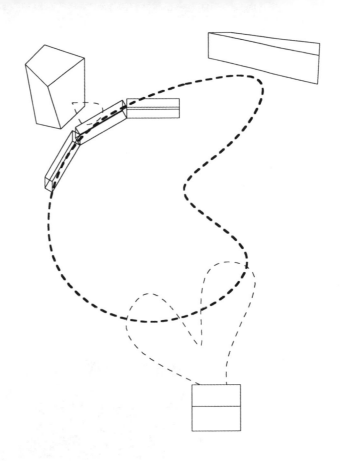

talking buildings and listening tram

what kind of place is the internet?

what kind of place would you like it to be?

Atmospheric? I would like it to be a good, nice place, where I could meet nice, wise people.

I am concerned bout misuse (pornography and too much commercials.

A meeting place, helping against isolation

As I said on a nother day, I am so new in this game that I don't have many wishes!

Crowded, anarchy

Better organised! Easier to find serious/correct information

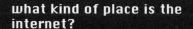

Billboards provoke discussions in public spaces...

the latest announcements from the info-boudoir sent waves of concern through the crowd ...

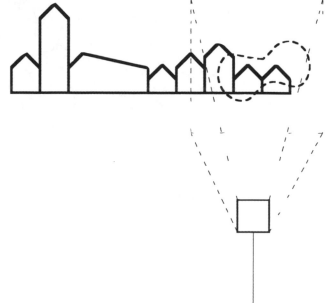

psychogeographic filters (de-tourism); pollution, poverty, violence...

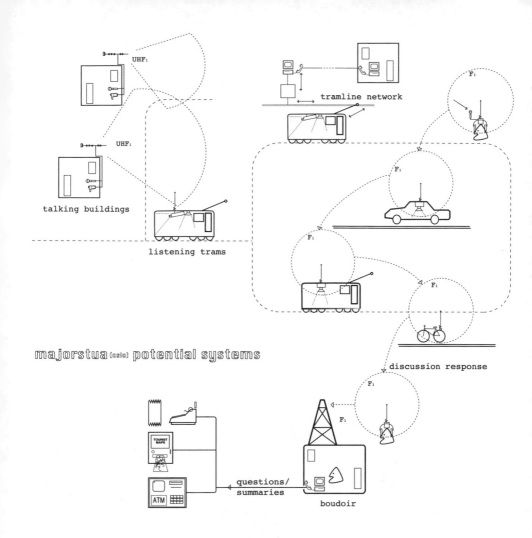

UHF₁

tramline network

talking buildings

listening trams

discussion response

majorstua (oslo) potential systems

questions/
summaries

boudoir

NEURAL-NETS

In the 1960s and 1970s, the predominant focus of experimental psychology in the United States turned from behaviourist stimulus-response paradigms to questions of how information is stored and processed in the mind. This was motivated, in part, by the belief that behavioural conditioning was inadequate to explain many human capabilities – a line of criticism sparked by Noam Chomsky's analysis of language learning – and thus that explanations must incorporate the 'invisible' mental processes the behaviourists had rejected.

The shift from behaviourist to cognitive psychology, as the new approach came to be known, was also driven by the advent of digital computing, which soon dominated as a paradigmatic model of the mind. Accounts of memory, for instance, relied heavily on this metaphor. Incoming information was said to be held in a sensory store, like an IO buffer, before being transferred to short-term memory, analogous to a computer's RAM, and from there possibly to long-term memory, functionally the mind's hard-drive.

From this perspective, a fundamental issue is how knowledge is represented and processed in the mind-computer. If knowledge is stored in our memory, then there must be some sort of record of the vast range of concepts – dogs, Idaho, love, green – we might have. What are the properties of these records? What happens when they are activated via input from the physical world (e.g. perception) or internally through reminding? How are they processed to achieve problem-solving?

One influential class of models was based on the idea of semantic networks, in which concepts are seen as nodes in a structure that links them to other concepts. For instance, the concept 'dog' might be linked to the concepts 'bark', 'tail', and 'fleas', so that each is defined in terms of the others. If the networks are hierarchical, so that 'dog' belongs to the class of 'animals,' which belongs to the class of 'living things', etc., then attributes might be inherited from superordinate to subordinate categories. When a concept is activated, those to which it is linked also receive some activation. Thus if one hears a bark and sees a tail and four legs, the concepts 'tail', 'bark', and 'legs' will pass activation to the concept 'dog', facilitating its recognition. Activation can also spread from the top down, so that if the concept 'animal' is primed, concepts such as 'dog', 'tail', and 'barks' will be more quickly triggered by perceptual evidence.

Accounts based on spreading activation through semantic networks agree with a good deal of behavioural data about how people recognise and recall concepts, but they have several limitations. First, semantic net models do not include learning mechanisms to explain how concepts are acquired and how new links emerge and change. Second, because there is a one-to-one mapping of concepts to nodes, any damage to the network will result in complete loss of functionality related to specific concepts. This is neither desirable in its own right, nor representative of behavioural data which shows a more graceful degradation with brain damage. Third, while semantic nets can represent propositional knowledge such as 'shoes are worn on feet,' they cannot handle procedural knowledge such as how to tie one's shoes, nor perceptual pattern-matching allowing shoes to be recognised from other visual stimulus in the first place. These tasks require specialised forms of representation and processing, and the resulting proliferation of models seems neither parsimonious nor plausible. Neural net models developed from a consideration of the flaws of semantic networks, coupled with an attempt to abstract the basic features of neural processing. Like semantic networks, neural net systems (also called parallel distributed processing or connectionist models to emphasise various of their features) are based on the idea of nodes which spread activation to each other along links. Each link has an associated weight representing the precise influence one node will have on another. Not only are these weights graded in intensity to reflect how closely related concepts are, but they may be positive or negative to reflect whether the concepts are in agreement or opposed. For instance, a two-layer net in which the bottom layer represents features such as 'tail', 'barks', 'legs', might be connected to a top layer representing animals such as 'dog', 'cat', and 'snake'. Activating 'tail' would pass activation to all three higher-level nodes. Activating 'bark', on the other hand, would activate 'dog', but reduce the activation of 'cat' and 'snake'.

A powerful feature of neural nets is their ability to learn. In an early class of learning algorithms, for instance, an intermediate layer of nodes, called 'hidden units', is introduced between the input and output layers. Weights are initially set randomly, and input patterns corresponding to desired outputs are activated. The discrepancy between the resulting pattern of output activation and the desired pattern is used to automatically adjust the weights between the input, hidden, and output layers. Over time, the network not only learns to respond correctly to inputs on which it has been trained, but also to generalise this learning for new inputs.

Hidden units may not map in obvious ways to input and output nodes. Instead, when a given input unit is activated, it passes varying amounts of activation to each of the hidden units, which in turn pass varying amounts of activation to the outputs. Each hidden unit becomes partially responsible for representing a number of concepts – the input concepts to the degree that it is activated by them, and the output concepts to the degree that it passes activation to them. In this sense, the representation of a given concept is distributed over the hidden units. It is easy to see by imagining that the input units corresponding to 'tail', 'bark', etc, are themselves hidden units linked to still more basic levels of representation. In principle, concepts may be distributed over all units at any given level of a network.

Representations can not only be distributed over hidden units, but over any layer of nodes. This is easy to see by imagining that the input units corresponding to 'tail', 'bark', etc, are themselves hidden units linked to still more basic levels of representation. In principle, concepts may be distributed over all units at any given level of a network.

Distributed representations have significant advantages over the more traditional forms of information processing like semantic networks. Procedural as well as propositional representation can be handled by linking output units directly to motor activities (e.g muscles in humans, engines in robots). Distributed representations are particularly effective at performing perceptual pattern matching: using raw data such as pixel values as input, for instance, it is possible to train networks to perform handwriting or face recognition. Finally, because concepts are distributed over a network, no unit depends entirely on another. Instead, structure at each level depends on patterns over the entire preceding one.

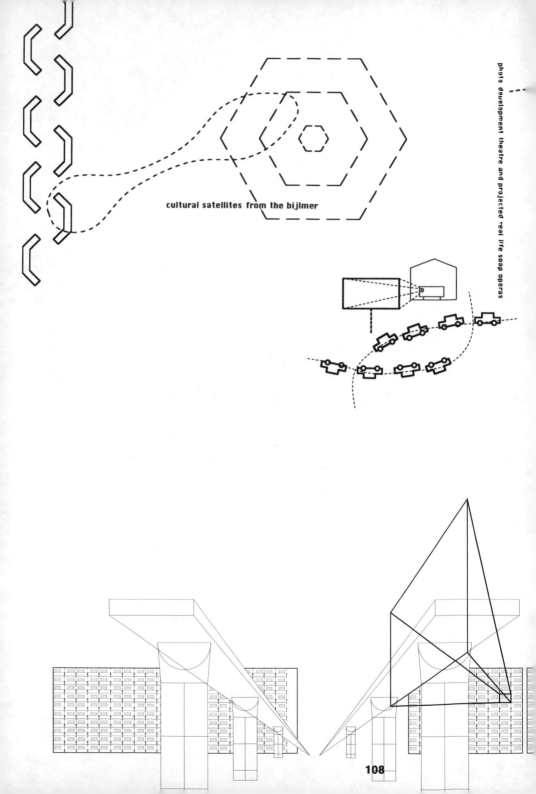

cultural satellites from the bijlmer

photo development theatre and projected real life soap operas

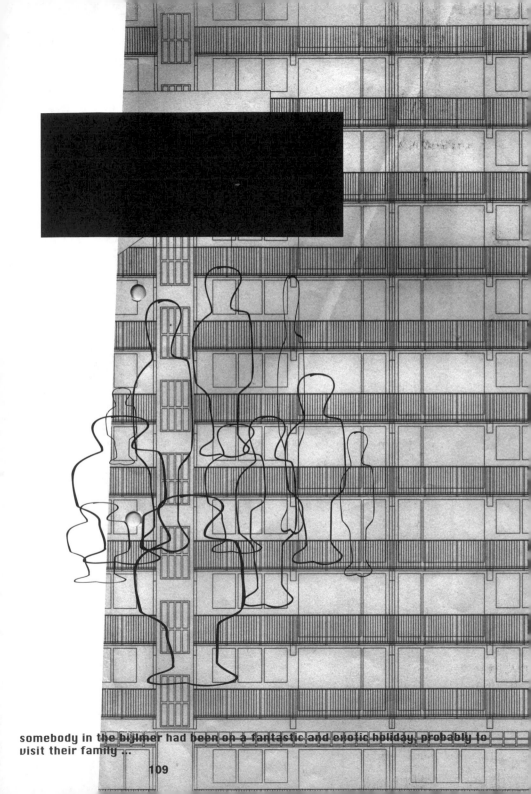

somebody in the bijlmer had been on a fantastic and exotic holiday, probably to visit their family ...

cages to which only elderly
people are given keys allow
them to enjoy public spaces
without anxiety.

mobile cages give security
to elderly pedestrians.

a variety of different styles
could be offered, from ornate
victorian castings to stream-
lined modern shapes

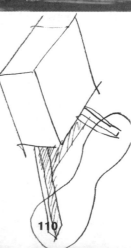

ELDERLY
GRAFITI

↓

psycho geographic maps

↓

tattoo landscape

control

red

The psychogeographic radio overlay was being abused by muggers who managed to steal a couple of anxiety pagers and were creating zones of fear everywhere...

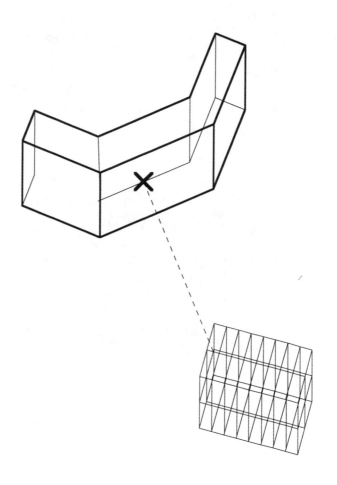

cage and pointer: protection, stigmata amd urban warfare

MUGGER

WINDOWS ⑦ IXELS FOR ⲱⲇ Ds ~ ⌐8 ⑦

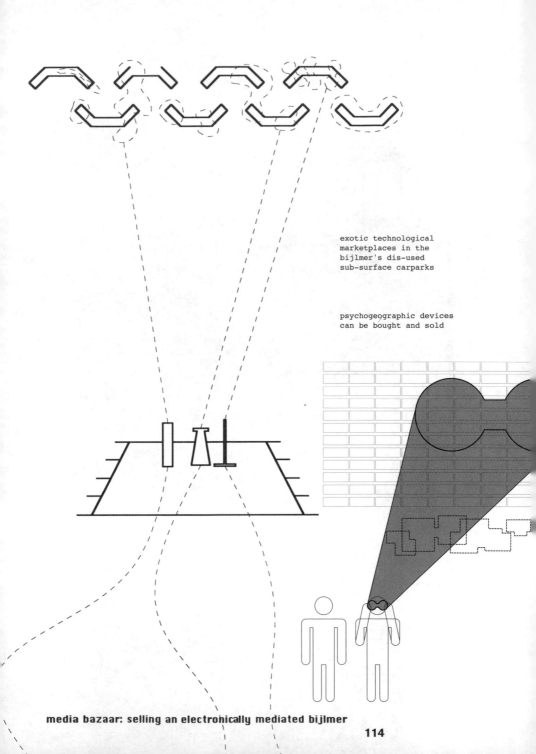

exotic technological
marketplaces in the
bijlmer's dis-used
sub-surface carparks

psychogeographic devices
can be bought and sold

media bazaar: selling an electronically mediated bijlmer

114

the market becomes a centre for interbijlmer gadgetry such as lamp post switches, scanning lightbulbs..........

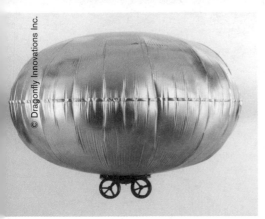

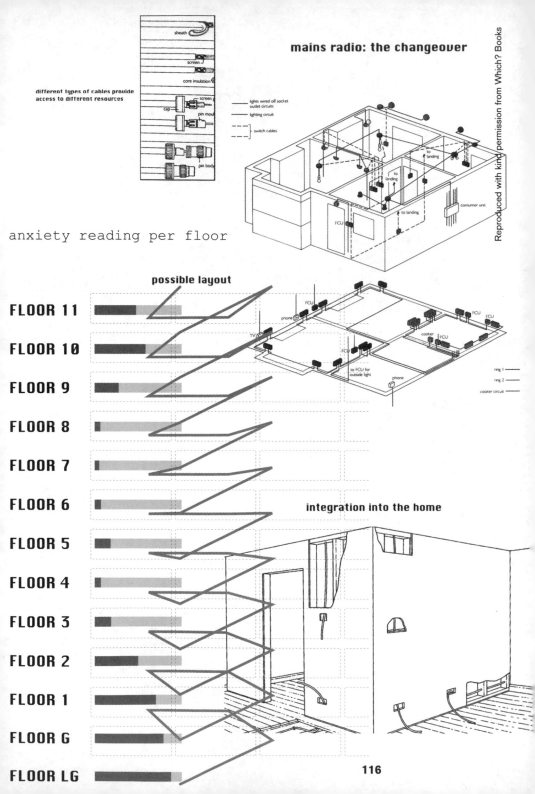

different types of cables provide
access to different resources

sheath
screen
core insulation
cap
screen
pin mou[nt]
pin body

mains radio: the changeover

lights wired off socket
outlet circuits
lighting circuit
switch cables

to landing
to landing
to landing
consumer unit
FCU

anxiety reading per floor

possible layout

FLOOR 11

FLOOR 10

FLOOR 9

FLOOR 8

FLOOR 7

FLOOR 6

FLOOR 5

FLOOR 4

FLOOR 3

FLOOR 2

FLOOR 1

FLOOR G

FLOOR LG

FCU
phone
TV/rn
FCU
to FCU for
outside light
phone
cooker
FCU
FCU
FCU
ring 1
ring 2
cooker circuit

integration into the home

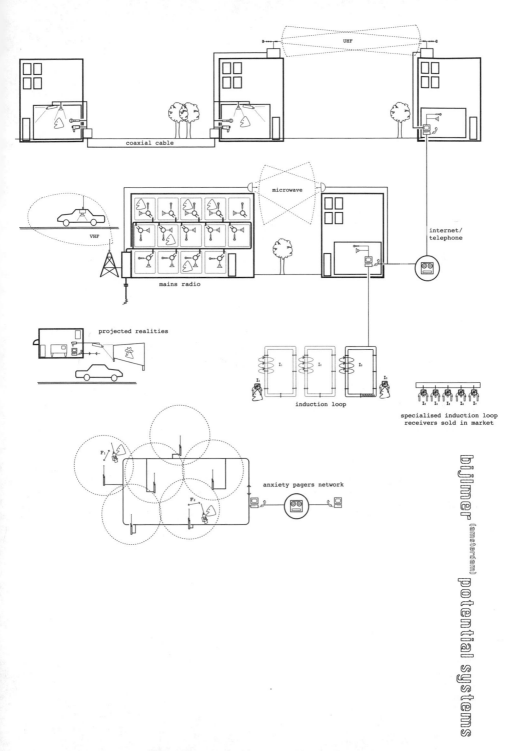

UHF

coaxial cable

microwave

VHF

internet/
telephone

mains radio

projected realities

induction loop

specialised induction loop
receivers sold in market

anxiety pagers network

bijlmer (amsterdam) potential systems

117

FINAL PROPOSALS FOR THE THREE SITES WERE SUMMARISED USING INTERACTIVE
DIAGRAMS, AREA OVERVIEWS, AND CATALOGUES OF POSSIBLE ARTEFACTS.

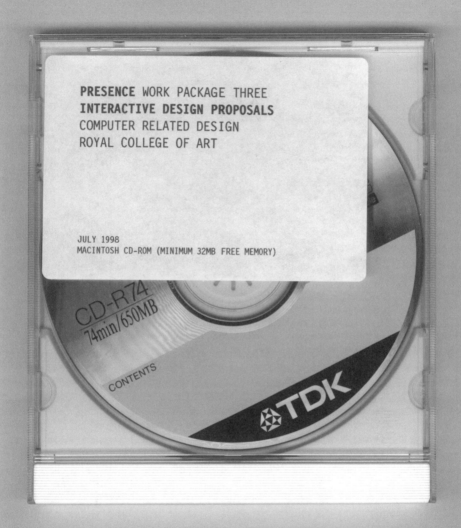

PRESENCE WORK PACKAGE THREE
INTERACTIVE DESIGN PROPOSALS
COMPUTER RELATED DESIGN
ROYAL COLLEGE OF ART

JULY 1998
MACINTOSH CD-ROM (MINIMUM 32MB FREE MEMORY)

CD-R74
74min/650MB

CONTENTS

TDK

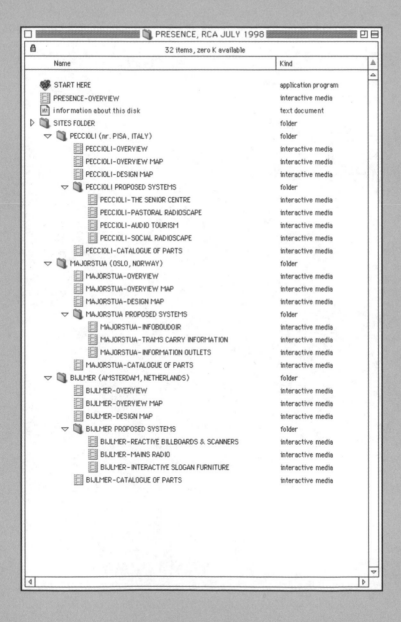

Name	Kind
PRESENCE, RCA JULY 1998	
32 items, zero K available	
START HERE	application program
PRESENCE-OVERVIEW	interactive media
information about this disk	text document
SITES FOLDER	folder
PECCIOLI (nr. PISA, ITALY)	folder
PECCIOLI-OVERVIEW	interactive media
PECCIOLI-OVERVIEW MAP	interactive media
PECCIOLI-DESIGN MAP	interactive media
PECCIOLI PROPOSED SYSTEMS	folder
PECCIOLI-THE SENIOR CENTRE	interactive media
PECCIOLI-PASTORAL RADIOSCAPE	interactive media
PECCIOLI-AUDIO TOURISM	interactive media
PECCIOLI-SOCIAL RADIOSCAPE	interactive media
PECCIOLI-CATALOGUE OF PARTS	interactive media
MAJORSTUA (OSLO, NORWAY)	folder
MAJORSTUA-OVERVIEW	interactive media
MAJORSTUA-OVERVIEW MAP	interactive media
MAJORSTUA-DESIGN MAP	interactive media
MAJORSTUA PROPOSED SYSTEMS	folder
MAJORSTUA-INFOBOUDOIR	interactive media
MAJORSTUA-TRAMS CARRY INFORMATION	interactive media
MAJORSTUA-INFORMATION OUTLETS	interactive media
MAJORSTUA-CATALOGUE OF PARTS	interactive media
BIJLMER (AMSTERDAM, NETHERLANDS)	folder
BIJLMER-OVERVIEW	interactive media
BIJLMER-OVERVIEW MAP	interactive media
BIJLMER-DESIGN MAP	interactive media
BIJLMER PROPOSED SYSTEMS	folder
BIJLMER-REACTIVE BILLBOARDS & SCANNERS	interactive media
BIJLMER-MAINS RADIO	interactive media
BIJLMER-INTERACTIVE SLOGAN FURNITURE	interactive media
BIJLMER-CATALOGUE OF PARTS	interactive media

☐ PECCIOLI (TUSCANY, ITALY) PROPOSED SYSTEMS

SENIOR CENTRE   AUDIO TOURISM   SOCIAL RADIO   PASTORAL RADIO

☐ SOCIAL RADIOSCAPE

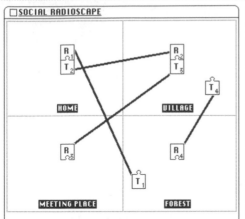

Pairs of detachable transmitters and receivers can be used to set up a wide variety of social networks. Transmitters can be detached and placed in different areas, or attached to other people's receivers. As loops and chains are formed, complex social spaces can be accessed.

☐ AUDIO TOURISM

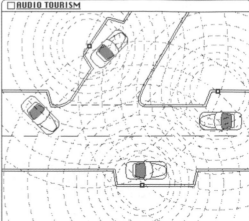

Tuning to the local radioscape plays the region's ambience. Pulling into a sonic lay-by allows more place-specific sounds to be heard, while a layered soundscape builds up as drivers approach the village itself.

☐ THE SENIOR CENTRE

1 Shelf with listening devices.
2 Directional listening devices.
3 Radioscape telephone.
4 Long listening bench.
5 CD player and landscape CD selection.
6 Listening device.
7 CD archive.
8 Radiostation conference room.
9 Social radioscape receiver.
10 Social radioscape transmittor.

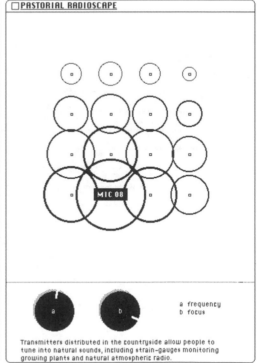

The Senior Centre in Peccioli. Special furniture is provided to access the radioscape, craft sounds for the touristic radioscape, and maintain social radioscape equipment.

☐ PASTORIAL RADIOSCAPE

MIC 08

a frequency
b focus

Transmitters distributed in the countryside allow people to tune into natural sounds, including strain-gauges monitoring growing plants and natural atmospheric radio.

In Peccioli, social, pastoral, and touristic radioscapes offer the village elders new ways to enjoy their environment. The hub of this activity is the Senior Centre, a place to check out equipment, edit sounds for visitors, or use special listening furniture.

THE TRAM NETWORK INFO—BOUDOIR INFORMATION OUTLETS

☐ INFO BOUDOIR

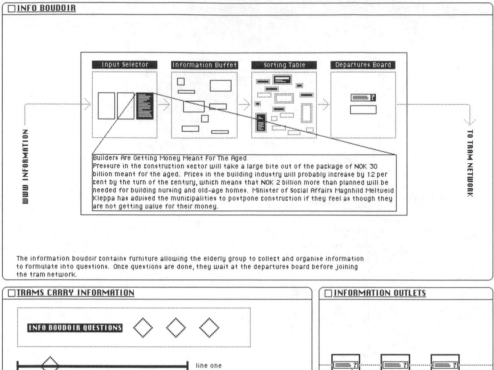

Input Selector   Information Buffet   Sorting Table   Departures Board

WWW INFORMATION

TO TRAM NETWORK

Builders Are Getting Money Meant For The Aged
Pressure in the construction sector will take a large bite out of the package of NOK 30
billion meant for the aged. Prices in the building industry will probably increase by 12 per
cent by the turn of the century, which means that NOK 2 billion more than planned will be
needed for building nursing and old-age homes. Minister of Social Affairs Magnhild Meltveid
Kleppa has advised the municipalities to postpone construction if they feel as though they
are not getting value for their money.

The information boudoir contains furniture allowing the elderly group to collect and organise information
to formulate into questions. Once questions are done, they wait at the departures board before joining
the tram network.

☐ TRAMS CARRY INFORMATION

INFO BOUDOIR QUESTIONS

line one
line two
line three
line four
line five
line six
line seven

Trams carry questions to stops, where they are transmitted to devices at the
stops. They may be sent to nearby cafés or telephone boxes, before the next
tram comes and picks them up.

☐ INFORMATION OUTLETS

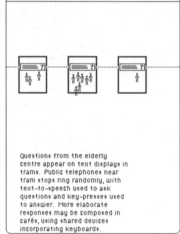

Questions from the elderly
centre appear on text displays in
trams. Public telephones near
tram stops ring randomly, with
text-to-speech used to ask
questions and key-presses used
to answer. More elaborate
responses may be composed in
cafés, using shared devices
incorporating keyboards.

In Oslo, the elders mediate a district-wide political discussion. Using special information furniture in the
library, they formulate questions which circulate through the locality via the tram system. Answered
questions return to be reported or rephrased into new queries.

☐ REACTIVE BILLBOARDS & SCANNERS

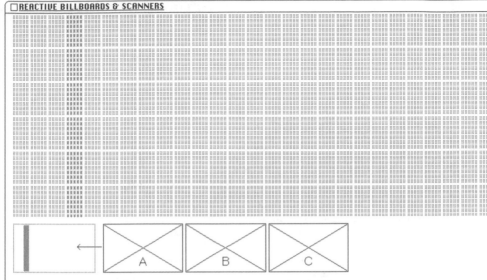

Billboards along the greater and lesser roads surrounding the Bijlmer display images scanned by the elders. Automatically selected to reflect the moods revealed by nearby sloganboards, they give outsiders an intimate view of life in the Bijlmer, challenging its dangerous reputation.

☐ INTERACTIVE SLOGAN FURNITURE

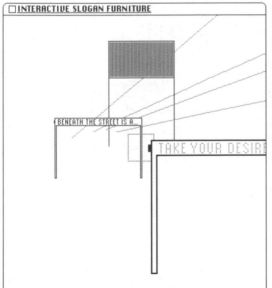

BENEATH THE STREET IS A.

TAKE YOUR DESIRE

Sloganboards are distributed in public spaces. Responding to mains radio devices used by people in their flats, or overwritten by passer-bys, they reveal and provoke local attitudes.

☐ MAINS RADIO

positive-negative   active-passive   personal-impersonal

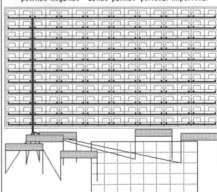

A variety of devices plug into the mains radio system running in the apartment blocks. People select images or slogans; their choices are taken as a measure of their emotions.

In the Bijlmer, publicly-displayed images and slogans reflect the local mood. A network allows expressions to spread from the personal to the public, increasing social coherence and letting outsiders see behind the area's exaggerated notoriety.

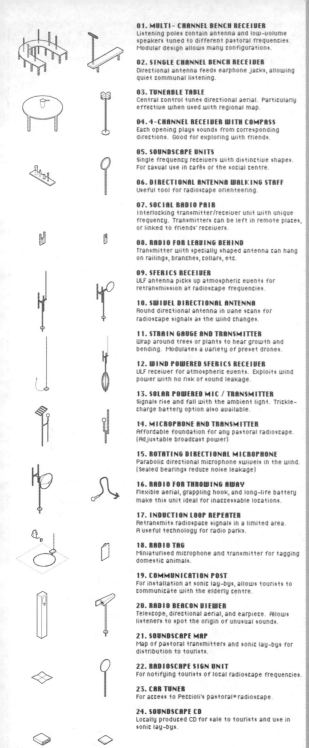

01. MULTI-CHANNEL BENCH RECEIVER
Listening poles contain antenna and low-volume speakers tuned to different pastoral frequencies. Modular design allows many configurations.

02. SINGLE CHANNEL BENCH RECEIVER
Directional antenna feeds earphone jacks, allowing quiet communal listening.

03. TUNEABLE TABLE
Central control tunes directional aerial. Particularly effective when used with regional map.

04. 4-CHANNEL RECEIVER WITH COMPASS
Each opening plays sounds from corresponding directions. Good for exploring with friends.

05. SOUNDSCAPE UNITS
Single frequency receivers with distinctive shapes. For casual use in cafés or the social centre.

06. DIRECTIONAL ANTENNA WALKING STAFF
Useful tool for radioscape orienteering.

07. SOCIAL RADIO PAIR
Interlocking transmitter/receiver unit with unique frequency. Transmitters can be left in remote places, or linked to friends' receivers.

08. RADIO FOR LEAVING BEHIND
Transmitter with specially shaped antenna can hang on railings, branches, collars, etc.

09. SFERICS RECEIVER
ULF antenna picks up atmospheric events for retransmission at radioscape frequencies.

10. SWIVEL DIRECTIONAL ANTENNA
Round directional antenna in vane scans for radioscape signals as the wind changes.

11. STRAIN GAUGE AND TRANSMITTER
Wrap around trees or plants to hear growth and bending. Modulates a variety of preset drones.

12. WIND POWERED SFERICS RECEIVER
ULF receiver for atmospheric events. Exploits wind power with no risk of sound leakage.

13. SOLAR POWERED MIC / TRANSMITTER
Signals rise and fall with the ambient light. Trickle-charge battery option also available.

14. MICROPHONE AND TRANSMITTER
Affordable foundation for any pastoral radioscape. (Adjustable broadcast power)

15. ROTATING DIRECTIONAL MICROPHONE
Parabolic directional microphone swivels in the wind. (Sealed bearings reduce noise leakage)

16. RADIO FOR THROWING AWAY
Flexible aerial, grappling hook, and long-life battery make this unit ideal for inaccessable locations.

17. INDUCTION LOOP REPEATER
Retransmits radiospace signals in a limited area. A useful technology for radio parks.

18. RADIO TAG
Miniaturised microphone and transmitter for tagging domestic animals.

19. COMMUNICATION POST
For installation at sonic lay-bys, allows tourists to communicate with the elderly centre.

20. RADIO BEACON VIEWER
Telescope, directional aerial, and earpiece. Allows listeners to spot the origin of unusual sounds.

21. SOUNDSCAPE MAP
Map of pastoral transmitters and sonic lay-bys for distribution to tourists.

22. RADIOSCAPE SIGN UNIT
For notifying tourists of local radioscape frequencies.

23. CAR TUNER
For access to Peccioli's pastoral*radioscape.

24. SOUNDSCAPE CD
Locally produced CD for sale to tourists and use in sonic lay-bys.

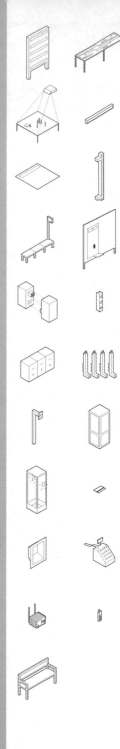

01. QUESTION ARRIVAL/DEPARTURE UNIT
As departure board, allows last-minute cancellations or delays. As arrivals board, incoming question/answers are signalled by a quiet bell.

02. INFORMATION BUFFET UNIT
Multiple text screens allow groups to browse and select incoming information.

03. INFORMATION SORTING TABLE
Allows text and graphics to be input, moved, or edited. Ideal for group use.

04. STANDARD TEXT UNIT
Standard horizontal format, with 52 character display.

05. PAVING STONE TEXT UNIT
Incorporates high-impact display. Pressure sensitive response paving also available.

06. VERTICAL TEXT UNIT
Flexible 40-character unit suitable for low spaces.

07. MODULAR QUESTION BENCH
Basic unit integrating screen, electronics, and seating reduces clutter in busy street areas.

08. POLITICAL TRAM STOP
Standard query-response unit with trams communications and windscreen. Large area permits displays of maps or advertising.

09. INFRA-RED DATA TRANSFER POINTS
Reciprical units for installation on trams and stops. Permits rapid transfer of questions and answers. (Supplied singly)

10. CLIP-ON RESPONSE UNIT
Applies easily to standard tram railings; wireless communications to tram-mounted question boards.

11. POLITICAL TICKET UNIT stamping tickets automatically registers responses. (For use near question boards)

12. WHISPERING HAND STRAPS
Low volume text-to-speech with manual response buttons.

13. VOICE INPUT UNIT
Speech-to-text allows detailed responses to be made easily. Indoor/outdoor use.

14. POLITICAL PHONE BOX
Tram stop units randomly dial public phones, collecting key-press responses from passer-bys.

15. TALKING PHONE BOX
Attachments allow questions to be asked and answered without entering boxes.

16. POLITICAL PHONE CARD
Automatically dials boudoir speech-to-text response line. Well-suited for promotional uses.

17. POLITICAL ATM
Questions are displayed while transactions are processed, with responses collected using standard (accept/correct/cancel) keys.

18. POLITICAL CASH MACHINE
Questions and response summaries are printed on the back of receipts.

19. POST CARD RACK
Holds approx. 300 freepost response cards, for installation near question boards.

20. SMS PHONE
Allows detailed responses to questions. May be limited to communication with tram stop units.

21. BENCH FOR FAILED QUESTIONS
Text screen shows questions transferred to wait for attention. Ideal for sites overlooking the sea.

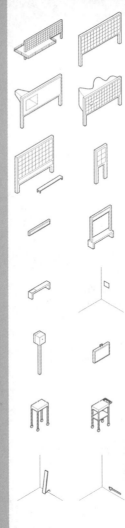

01. 96 SHEET BILLBOARD WITH PLATFORM
Built-in platform affords gardening, social gatherings, games. Useful for reinforcing imagery about life in the Bijlmer.

02. 270 NETWORK STANDARD BILLBOARD
Large image board for use by major roads. LED, video, or mechanical flap options available.

03. IMAGE BOARD WITH VIEWING WINDOW
Allows images to be visually linked with relevant views (e.g., housing blocks, lakes).

04. 270 NETWORK BILLBOARD WITH CABIN
Useful meeting space for gauging reactions or planning new campaigns. (With viewing port)

05. BILLBOARD W/ TEXT AND VIEWING UNITS
Integrated text board for displaying associated slogans. Useful for commuter routes.

06. 6 SHEET DISPLAY UNIT
Pedestrian image board for use on small roadways. Intimate size also viewable from slow-moving cars.

07. STANDARD TEXT UNIT
Basic slogan display for installation on walls, existing poles, etc.

08. SLOGAN BENCH
Sloganboard with integrated bench. Sensible configuration for parks and walkways.

09. SCANNING BENCH
For use in the senior centre. (Outdoor use not recommended)

10. BUILT-IN SCANNER
Space-saving configuration scans documents, images, faces pressed to surface.

11. PIN-HOLE SCANNER UNIT
For portrature, social events, landscapes, etc.

12. PORTABLE SCANNER UNIT
The elder facilitators may use these for scanning in private flats, etc. (Mains-radio aware)

13. SCANNER TABLE UNIT
Rolling table scanners, easy to transport through the long paths and hallways of the Bijlmermeer housing blocks.

14. SCANNER TROLLEY UNIT
Upper unit contains scanner, oriented to capture images or objects placed on the lower shelf.

15. MAINS RADIO INPUT DEVICE (TYPE A)
Plugs directly into the mains radio data system. Allows selection of images and slogans from the central database.

16. MAINS RADIO INPUT DEVICE (TYPE B)
Image viewer slides horizontally, "scanning" images and slogans.

17. PSYCHOGEOGRAPHIC MAP
Plots emotional topography compiled from mains radio and sloganboard activity.

Experiments

After the first year of the project, we had focused and elaborated proposals for each of the three communities. The Pastoral Radioscape would allow people in Peccioli to listen to the surrounding countryside, to communicate using a social radio web, and to transmit sounds, music and stories to roadside lay-bys for tourists to hear. The Digital Boudoir would allow older people in Oslo to publish questions to appear in public spaces and collect the results. And in the Bijlmer, the Projected Realities network would create an electronic facade for the area, with devices linking from people's homes, through local neighbourhoods, to roadways ringing the area.

Having developed the proposals with inspiration from the Probe returns and comments from local older people, we believed our ideas reflected the three communities in sensitive but unexpected ways. Moreover, the proposals excited us because they opened new ground for design. They challenged assumptions about communications technologies, about technologies used in public spaces, and about older people. Although they were developed with close attention to the specifics of the three sites, we felt the ideas behind them could be relevant for many other situations.

At this stage we tested approximate versions of the systems in the three sites. Despite our enthusiasm, it was clear that the proposals would have to be further developed to tune them practically and aesthetically to the three sites. We had also begun to realise that it would be impossible to implement working prototypes for each of the three sites. Time and money required that we focus our efforts on one, and we needed some way to decide among them.

We were not primarily concerned with technical practicalities at this stage, as we were satisfied that a number of possible routes existed to realise each of the proposals. Instead, we focused on using appropriate, often low-tech, means to simulate and test the experiences the proposals would engender – their aesthetics, their social effects, and their cultural implications – with the older people in the three communities. Nonetheless, in the course of the experiments it became clear that both technical concerns and the intellectual challenge offered by the systems would play a large role in deciding which to take forward.

RECONNOITRING THE PECCIOLI RADIOSCAPE / We flew to Italy with a good deal of equipment, prepared to test our ideas about using radio to enhance the enjoyment Peccioli's older people found in their surroundings. Large-scale topographic maps were prepared to help us ask the older citizens where we might locate interesting soundscapes. A parabolic microphone and high-quality cassette recorder would allow us to capture the sounds. Most potent of all, we brought a twenty watt FM transmitter and associated equipment, prepared to broadcast the results of our experiment to the older people in the village or while they drove with us around the countryside.

Our research into the legality of broadcasting sounds of the countryside over FM frequencies in Italy had been frustrating and inconclusive. Attempts to locate the relevant authorities over the month before we travelled had been unsuccessful, despite the help of a native Italian to guide and translate for us. We knew that in many countries low-powered broadcasts are legal (though a twenty watt transmitter, capable of being received for at least ten miles, was pushing the limits). But the situation in Italy was unclear. It seemed that either anything was legal, or nothing was. Given that our tests would take place only over a day or two, in a fairly remote village, we decided to risk detection and proceed with the trials.

Meeting with the local group of older people, we spent an afternoon poring over the topological maps, marking them with farms, streams, and other sites where we might discover interesting sites to harvest sounds. As we looked over the maps, the local group regaled us with stories of wartime hardships, local feuds, and changing boundaries caused by economic swings. As they pointed out the relevant areas from a rooftop terrace, it became increasingly evident that there was a social and political element to choosing sites for the Pastoral Landscape, one that could enrich the experience of hearing sounds from locations within sight of the village.

The next day, we returned to the village to start recording the rural soundscape. Accompanied by our local partners and several of the older inhabitants, we traversed the countryside near Peccioli, stopping at spots identified by the local group to sample the ambient sounds. A local villa yielded bird songs from a nearby wood. A stream near the community dump – source of much of the village's income – provided water sounds. Sheep at a local farm bleated, and chickens clucked. We learned quickly that exposed viewpoints are not good listening points, as they are contaminated by air and road traffic. But over the day we gathered a good collection of sounds for transmission.

Unfortunately, the issue of illegal broadcasting had been simmering in the background during the visit. Our local partners, alarmed by our plans to set up the transmitter with its two metre aerial, had objected to its use from our arrival. As our preliminary meeting progressed, they built their argument. Many major radio stations had signal repeaters on a hillside only tens of kilometres away, they pointed out, allowing broadcasts to reach from Florence to Pisa. The airwaves were saturated, and a careful check confirmed that there were virtually no gaps in the spectrum. The radio landscape was in corporate hands: trespassing on it was bound to interfere with commercial broadcasts, and would likely bring complaints and even legal action. Although it was tempting to proceed regardless, our local partners, who would not be leaving the country the next day, grew increasingly desperate to stop us. In the end we relented. The Radioscape would not be tested during the trip.

The political impracticality of transmitting over commercial frequencies was disappointing. Solutions exist, but none are entirely satisfactory. Local radio stations might be willing to broadcast the soundscape periodically during the day, but this would interfere with the continuous availability that makes the Radioscape an extension of the landscape rather than a special event. More promising, the Radioscape could be transmitted over frequencies set aside for amateur use, and the older people provided with specialised receivers for listening, foreshadowing possibilities opened by digital radio. Although this has the advantage of creating a dedicated Radioscape, the sound quality would be reduced. Commercial interests only relinquish second-rate electromagnetic real estate to the public, devitalising autonomous uses of the airwaves.

If the Radioscape was unfeasible for practical reasons, however, its desirability was underscored by our tests. In wandering the countryside's ambient soundscape, we gave flesh to the sketches, diagrams, and particularly the interactive simulation with which we had explored the initial proposal for a Pastoral Radioscape. Focusing on recording heightened our awareness of the landscape as an auditory experience, and we began to appreciate the diversity of sounds we could find there. Most importantly, the group of older people joined us in our exploration. Not only did they use the maps to point out locations we might search for sounds, but they joined us on our expedition into the countryside, helping us locate suitable sites for recording, negotiating with local farmers to give us access to the animals, and listening to the results with enjoyment. This success actually helped dissuade us from pursuing the system further: convinced that it would work, we saw little intellectual challenge in attacking purely political obstacles to its development.

PROVOKING THE MAJORSTUA / Our proposal for Oslo called for equipment to be developed for the local library's Internet club, where the local group of older people met, and for trams and public spots in the area. The library would be equipped with special furniture allowing the older people to receive messages from local politicians and to scan the Internet in search of relevant issues. Other furniture would support them in working together to formulate questions from the information they had found. Special equipment would relay these questions to local trams, where they would ride through the district before disembarking to be sent to devices in tram stops and local restaurants and shops.

Despite the variety of technological paraphernalia proposed to realise the proposal, at heart the Digital Boudoir was a scheme to provoke communication between the older citizens and other inhabitants in the area. In testing the ideas, then, we concentrated on finding a way to simulate the sociopolitical effects of the system, rather than its technical underpinnings.

Meeting with the older people in the library, we distributed a series of cards that we had prepared, each with a paragraph or captioned image addressing an issue gleaned from the Internet. The issues were relevant to the Majorstua when possible, Oslo, or Norway at the most general, in order to emphasise the situated nature of the system we envisioned. Using the cards as inspiration, the group was asked to think of questions they might want to ask their fellow citizens.

As with Peccioli, we had prepared apparatus for the experiment. In this case, the most significant piece of equipment was a PC-based telemarketing system, allowing phones to be dialled and a limited, pre-scripted interaction to be pursued automatically. We recorded the older people asking their questions, and added a brief introduction ("Don't hang up! Please answer the following question"), and instructions for answering using the phone's keypad. Having collected the phone numbers of all the public telephone booths in the district, our experimental set up was complete.

The following day, we ran the experiment itself. Setting the software to systematically dial each of the telephone booths in turn, and to poll anybody answering with one of the older people's questions, we waited to see what would happen.

The results were disappointing. We soon found, for instance, that the dialling keys on Norwegian pay-phones are disconnected when a call is received. Presumably useful in preventing conversations from being interrupted, it meant that we could not ask respondents to key in the answers to the older people's questions. Instead, we had to record new instructions asking people to speak their answers, and set the system to automatically record when a reply was heard.

Still we received no answers to our queries. A quick reconnaissance of local pay phones revealed that they rang very quietly when a call was received. Local passers-by would be unlikely to hear them, especially in the well-frequented areas near the train station and along the busy roads that we had targeted particularly. We switched our attention to phones in less populated areas, reasoning that even if there were fewer people around, they would be more likely to notice the calls.

Our calls remained unanswered. People ignored the ringing phones, and if they did answer soon hung up. With several of our team observing the phone booths we were by now targeting directly, we realised that the phones were only answered when somebody was in the booth about to make a call anyway.

Finally it dawned on us that when a public phone rings, the one thing certain is that it's not for you. The volume of the ring or location of the booth is irrelevant unless the possibility of an incoming call being meaningful is conveyed clearly. Although we had attached cards announcing the experiment ('if the phone rings, please pick it up ...') in each of the local telephone booths, they were apparently not sufficiently noticeable. People didn't participate in the experiment simply because they were unaware that the experiment was going on.

Despite the almost complete failure of the test – we received only two meaningful answers from the hundreds of calls we placed – we were paradoxically enthused by the experience. There seemed several avenues towards making the system work. As one of our partners was from the local telecom company, it seemed possible to arrange for the ringing tones on public phones to be raised slightly. Notices could be placed in the booths explaining the system, and the local print and broadcast media might be enlisted to help announce it. Special booths might even be identified, painted and labelled to mark them out as the centre of the polling. As an occasion for evaluation, the Digital Boudoir experiment was clearly a failure. But as an opportunity to advance our thinking, it was useful and even inspiring.

INTERVENING IN THE BIJLMER / For our final experiment in the Netherlands, we travelled with 100 sheets of card stock, each cut to about a half by two metres and bound into blocks of twenty, as well as other more manageable materials.

Our meeting with the older inhabitants had been prepared by the local partners. Each of the older people had been given a disposable camera with which to take pictures from around the Bijlmer, and had been encouraged to bring their own snapshots and artefacts to our gathering. Using a digital scanner, we captured more than a hundred images over the course of the visit and during the meeting itself. Taking advantage of the unique properties of scanners as a kind of horizontal camera, we also captured images of the older participants' hands, and some of the things they were carrying with them, such as spectacles, jewellery, and papers, as a way of giving a more intimate glimpse into their lives.

We had also brought small booklets printed with slogans which we distributed to the group at the beginning of the meeting. Made up of fragments of local replies to the Cultural Probes ('I miss being able to go to the sea'), as well as phrases from a variety of other sources, the booklets were designed to prompt discussion of the kinds of statements the group might want to make about their lives in the Bijlmer.

Discussing appropriate statements and images led to a wide-ranging (and heated) discussion about conditions in the area: the persistence of racism, the difficulty of getting help from police, and the misunderstandings of outsiders. Already the Projected Realities concept had sparked reflective discussions about the Bijlmer, at least among the group of older inhabitants itself.

After the meeting, we retired to our local partners' offices to prepare for the next day's test. We sorted and scanned dozens of images, and selected and edited slogans from the many suggestions produced by the group. Once we had our final selection of slogans, we spent the rest of the evening printing them out and mounting them onto the boards we had brought. By the end of the night, we had a collection of ten sets of nine slogans ready to be tested in the Bijlmer.

On the way to the area the following morning, we picked up the remaining elements of our experimental apparatus: ten clothes stands rented from a local firm. At the Bijlmer, we constructed our test rig, hanging the sets of cards from the stands to make our simple slogan boards. We wheeled them into the space outside the local social centre, a paved area covered by an overhead roadway, that connected a local car park and tram station with a shopping centre. There we waited to gauge the reaction of local passers-by.

Standing near large coat racks hung with cards making various statements soon made us feel uncomfortably exposed. We found ourselves embarrassed by some of the slogans. They seemed the product of religious fanaticism ('treat others as you would like to be treated'), crude political protest ('people ignore us in the Bijlmer'), or of a naive vulnerability ('I am afraid'). We began to realise that the best slogans were slightly ambiguous or detached in tone ('I am from another country'), or were particular and personal statements ('I like a few drinks once in a while'). These seemed to escape classification into known forms of public display, invoking curiosity and imagination rather than immediate dismissal.

Despite our initial trepidation, people in the area responded extremely well to the test. Smiling and curious as they walked past, many stopped to flip through the slogans and discuss their intention with us. They told us of their lives in the Bijlmer, its history, and its prospects, and filled out cards we had brought along asking for reactions to the test, suggesting new slogans ('if you don't like it here, it is your own fault') and urging us to install similar displays along the outskirts of the area – independently validating our original proposal.

As evening came, we prepared to test the second part of the system. We moved to a small booth on the platform of the local tram station, kindly provided to us by the local authorities after negotiations with our local partners. Using a high-powered data projector, we back-projected the images we had collected onto a window of the booth so that they could be seen by people as they disembarked and waited for trains.

As with the slogans, the experience of displaying images publicly revealed aspects of the experience that we hadn't anticipated. Most important was that, when displayed in a normal format, many of the snapshots provided by the older inhabitants were difficult to interpret. Rather than providing intriguing glimpses into the lives of the Bijlmer's diverse citizens, they appeared as a domestic slide show shown in an incongruous and unmotivated setting. Other images, notably scans of hands and personal artefacts, were more effective. Appearing as if someone were pressing against the display from another space, they provided a more peculiar and disquieting stimulus for speculation and discussion. We learned that in order to be effective, we would have to arrange for a future image display either to involve unusual images or display formats.

In contrast with the other two sites, the tests in the Bijlmer appeared to be unqualified successes. The older group participated with enthusiasm and became involved not only in discussions about the system, but the underlying issues it raised. Local inhabitants also engaged with the tests, welcoming their experimental nature and becoming involved in their aims and ideals. In part, the success of the Bijlmer test was due to the lack of any technical failures. Beyond this, however, the situation in the Bijlmer presented us with more complex and richer issues than the other sites, and it was the success of the ideas to raise these social and cultural issues that convinced us to pursue the system further.

SEVERAL DAYS WERE SPENT EXPLORING SOUNDSCAPES
NEAR PECCIOLI WITH LOCAL OLDER PEOPLE.

1. AUDIO CASSETTE RECORDER; 2. BLANK AUDIO CASSETTE; 3. DRY-WIPE MARKERS;
4. BINOCULARS; 5. LAMINATED MAP; 6. TRIPOD; 7. PARABOLIC MICROPHONE AND HEADPHONES;
8. FM RECEIVER; 9. GROUND PLANE TRANSMITTER AND TRIPOD-MOUNTED AERIAL;
10. STRONG ADHESIVE TAPE; 11. AERIAL CLIPS; 12. SHIELDED CABLING

Pod.º S. Francesco

GARGA...

Pod.ª Colombaia

Pod.ª Chiesino

LE SPINAIE

PIANO DI TAMBURINO

Pod.ª Paiole

Botro di ...

Pod.ª del Bosco

I PIANI FORTI

MORICCI

Pod.ª Moricci

Fotonor AS

IN OSLO WE USED A TELEMARKETING SYSTEM AND
PUBLIC PHONE BOXES TO TEST PROSPECTS FOR A
COMMUNITY CONVERSATION LED BY OLDER PEOPLE.

1. 'BIGMOUTH' TELE-MARKETING COMPUTER EXPANSION CARD; 2. 'BIGMOUTH' INSTRUCTION BOOK;
3. PC-COMPATIBLE COMPUTER; 4. DICTAPHONE AND TAPE; 5. DOMESTIC TELEPHONE;
6. SPEAKER MONITOR; 7. SCANDINAVIAN PHONE ADAPTOR; 8. PHONE BOX ADVERTISEMENT CARDS;
9. MAP OF OSLO; 10. MAP OF MAJORSTUA DISTRICT SHOWING PHONE BOX LOCATIONS

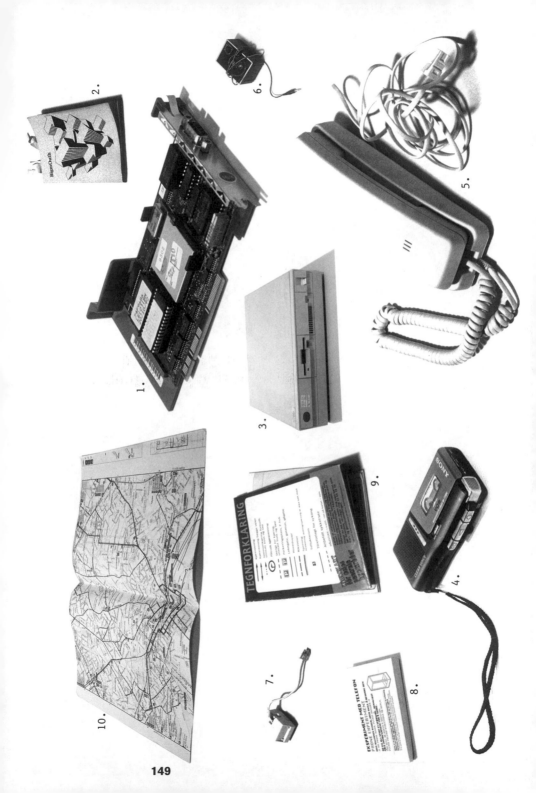

MAJORSTUA

```
 9:45:41AM10-20    4  TELEMARKETING BOX#100    ENTERED (HELLO)
 9:45:47AM10-20    5  TELEMARKETING BOX#110    ENTERED (QUESTION)
 9:45:55AM10-20    6  TELEMARKETING BOX#120    ENTERED (RECORD)
 9:46:03AM10-20    7 *MESSAGE  A011 LEFT  BOX#120    T= 00:04
 9:46:03AM10-20    8  TELEMARKETING BOX#130    ENTERED (GOODBYE)
 9:46:05AM10-20    9  MESSAGE DISTRIBUTED TO 22363333
 9:46:08AM10-20   10  DISTRIBUTION COMPLETED
 9:49:44AM10-20    4  DISTRIBUTION COMPLETED
 9:52:16AM10-20    4  TELEMARKETING BOX#100    ENTERED (HELLO)
 9:52:22AM10-20    5  TELEMARKETING BOX#110    ENTERED (QUESTION)
 9:52:30AM10-20    6  TELEMARKETING BOX#120    ENTERED (RECORD)
 9:52:36AM10-20    7  MESSAGE DISTRIBUTED TO 22567840
10:10:47AM10-20    8  TELEMARKETING BOX#100    ENTERED (HELLO)
10:10:54AM10-20    9  TELEMARKETING BOX#110    ENTERED (QUESTION)
10:11:01AM10-20   10  TELEMARKETING BOX#120    ENTERED (RECORD)
10:11:07AM10-20   11  MESSAGE DISTRIBUTED TO 22607559
10:14:23AM10-20   12  TELEMARKETING BOX#100    ENTERED (HELLO)
10:14:30AM10-20   13  TELEMARKETING BOX#110    ENTERED (QUESTION)
10:14:37AM10-20   14  TELEMARKETING BOX#120    ENTERED (RECORD)
10:14:47AM10-20   15 *MESSAGE  A012 LEFT  BOX#120    T= 00:05
10:14:47AM10-20   16  TELEMARKETING BOX#130    ENTERED (GOODBYE)
10:14:49AM10-20   17  MESSAGE DISTRIBUTED TO 22568277
10:16:00AM10-20   18  TELEMARKETING BOX#100    ENTERED (HELLO)
10:16:07AM10-20   19  TELEMARKETING BOX#110    ENTERED (QUESTION)
10:16:14AM10-20   20  TELEMARKETING BOX#120    ENTERED (RECORD)
10:16:20AM10-20   21  MESSAGE DISTRIBUTED TO 22604054
10:22:54AM10-20   22  TELEMARKETING BOX#100    ENTERED (HELLO)
10:23:01AM10-20   23  TELEMARKETING BOX#110    ENTERED (QUESTION)
10:23:08AM10-20   24  TELEMARKETING BOX#120    ENTERED (RECORD)
10:23:14AM10-20   25  MESSAGE DISTRIBUTED TO 22602435
11:00:34AM10-20    4  TELEMARKETING BOX#110    ENTERED (QUESTION)
11:00:46AM10-20    5  MESSAGE DISTRIBUTED TO 22363333
11:02:27AM10-20    4  TELEMARKETING BOX#110    ENTERED (QUESTION)
11:02:44AM10-20    5 *MESSAGE  A013 LEFT  BOX#110    T= 00:07
11:02:44AM10-20    6  TELEMARKETING BOX#130    ENTERED (GOODBYE)
11:02:46AM10-20    7  MESSAGE DISTRIBUTED TO 22363333
11:09:23AM10-20    8  TELEMARKETING BOX#110    ENTERED (QUESTION)
11:09:36AM10-20    9 *MESSAGE  A014 LEFT  BOX#110    T= 00:04
11:09:36AM10-20   10  TELEMARKETING BOX#130    ENTERED (GOODBYE)
11:09:38AM10-20   11  MESSAGE DISTRIBUTED TO 22604054
11:24:27AM10-20   12  TELEMARKETING BOX#110    ENTERED (QUESTION)
11:24:28AM10-20   13  MESSAGE DISTRIBUTED TO 22567840
11:30:11AM10-20   14  TELEMARKETING BOX#110    ENTERED (QUESTION)
11:30:21AM10-20   15  MESSAGE DISTRIBUTED TO 22605052
11:30:34AM10-20   16  TELEMARKETING BOX#110    ENTERED (QUESTION)
11:30:44AM10-20   17  MESSAGE DISTRIBUTED TO 22566280
11:34:30AM10-20   18  TELEMARKETING BOX#110    ENTERED (QUESTION)
11:34:50AM10-20   19 *MESSAGE  A015 LEFT  BOX#110    T= 00:11
11:34:50AM10-20   20  TELEMARKETING BOX#130    ENTERED (GOODBYE)
11:34:52AM10-20   21  MESSAGE DISTRIBUTED TO 22567204
11:35:18AM10-20   22  TELEMARKETING BOX#110    ENTERED (QUESTION)
11:35:29AM10-20   23  MESSAGE DISTRIBUTED TO 22607559
11:39:24AM10-20   24  TELEMARKETING BOX#110    ENTERED (QUESTION)
11:39:35AM10-20   25  MESSAGE DISTRIBUTED TO 22605058
11:42:35AM10-20   26  TELEMARKETING BOX#110    ENTERED (QUESTION)
11:42:46AM10-20   27  MESSAGE DISTRIBUTED TO 22607202
11:48:24AM10-20   28  TELEMARKETING BOX#110    ENTERED (QUESTION)
11:48:38AM10-20   29 *MESSAGE  A016 LEFT  BOX#110    T= 00:04
11:48:38AM10-20   30  TELEMARKETING BOX#130    ENTERED (GOODBYE)
11:48:40AM10-20   31  MESSAGE DISTRIBUTED TO 22603589
11:48:47AM10-20   32  TELEMARKETING BOX#110    ENTERED (QUESTION)
11:48:58AM10-20   33  MESSAGE DISTRIBUTED TO 22567648
11:49:12AM10-20   34  TELEMARKETING BOX#110    ENTERED (QUESTION)
11:49:26AM10-20   35 *MESSAGE  A017 LEFT  BOX#110    T= 00:04
11:49:26AM10-20   36  TELEMARKETING BOX#130    ENTERED (GOODBYE)
11:49:28AM10-20   37  MESSAGE DISTRIBUTED TO 22604862
12:15:45PM10-20    4  TELEMARKETING BOX#100    ENTERED (HELLO)
12:15:52PM10-20    5  TELEMARKETING BOX#110    ENTERED (QUESTION)
12:16:02PM10-20    6  MESSAGE DISTRIBUTED TO 22567840
12:17:41PM10-20    7  TELEMARKETING BOX#100    ENTERED (HELLO)
12:17:48PM10-20    8  TELEMARKETING BOX#110    ENTERED (QUESTION)
12:18:00PM10-20    9 *MESSAGE  A018 LEFT  BOX#110    T= 00:03
12:18:00PM10-20   10  TELEMARKETING BOX#130    ENTERED (GOODBYE)
12:18:02PM10-20   11  MESSAGE DISTRIBUTED TO 22604054
12:28:48PM10-20   12  TELEMARKETING BOX#100    ENTERED (HELLO)
12:28:55PM10-20   13  TELEMARKETING BOX#110    ENTERED (QUESTION)
12:29:06PM10-20   14  MESSAGE DISTRIBUTED TO 22567648
12:34:06PM10-20   15  TELEMARKETING BOX#100    ENTERED (HELLO)
12:34:13PM10-20   16  TELEMARKETING BOX#110    ENTERED (QUESTION)
12:34:23PM10-20   17  MESSAGE DISTRIBUTED TO 22603187
12:35:17PM10-20   18  TELEMARKETING BOX#100    ENTERED (HELLO)
12:35:24PM10-20   19  TELEMARKETING BOX#110    ENTERED (QUESTION)
12:35:41PM10-20   20 *MESSAGE  A019 LEFT  BOX#110    T= 00:08
12:35:41PM10-20   21  TELEMARKETING BOX#130    ENTERED (GOODBYE)
12:35:43PM10-20   22  MESSAGE DISTRIBUTED TO 22567840
12:36:34PM10-20   23  TELEMARKETING BOX#100    ENTERED (HELLO)
12:36:40PM10-20   24  TELEMARKETING BOX#110    ENTERED (QUESTION)
12:36:51PM10-20   25  MESSAGE DISTRIBUTED TO 22568277
12:37:23PM10-20   26  TELEMARKETING BOX#100    ENTERED (HELLO)
12:37:30PM10-20   27  TELEMARKETING BOX#110    ENTERED (QUESTION)
12:37:47PM10-20   28 *MESSAGE  A020 LEFT  BOX#110    T= 00:08
12:37:48PM10-20   29  TELEMARKETING BOX#130    ENTERED (GOODBYE)
12:37:49PM10-20   30  MESSAGE DISTRIBUTED TO 22363333
12:42:33PM10-20   31  TELEMARKETING BOX#100    ENTERED (HELLO)
12:42:38PM10-20   32  TELEMARKETING BOX#110    ENTERED (QUESTION)
12:42:46PM10-20   33  MESSAGE DISTRIBUTED TO 22607559
12:44:18PM10-20   34  TELEMARKETING BOX#100    ENTERED (HELLO)
12:44:23PM10-20   35  TELEMARKETING BOX#110    ENTERED (QUESTION)
12:44:33PM10-20   36 *MESSAGE  A021 LEFT  BOX#110    T= 00:04
12:44:33PM10-20   37  TELEMARKETING BOX#130    ENTERED (GOODBYE)
12:44:34PM10-20   38  MESSAGE DISTRIBUTED TO 22604862
12:45:34PM10-20   39  TELEMARKETING BOX#100    ENTERED (HELLO)
12:45:39PM10-20   40  TELEMARKETING BOX#110    ENTERED (QUESTION)
12:45:46PM10-20   41  MESSAGE DISTRIBUTED TO 22603187
12:55:51PM10-20   42  TELEMARKETING BOX#100    ENTERED (HELLO)
12:55:55PM10-20   43  TELEMARKETING BOX#110    ENTERED (QUESTION)
12:56:03PM10-20   44  MESSAGE DISTRIBUTED TO 22568317
 1:00:48PM10-20   45  TELEMARKETING BOX#100    ENTERED (HELLO)
 1:00:52PM10-20   46  TELEMARKETING BOX#110    ENTERED (QUESTION)
 1:01:00PM10-20   47  MESSAGE DISTRIBUTED TO 22604054
 1:01:13PM10-20   48  TELEMARKETING BOX#100    ENTERED (HELLO)
 1:01:17PM10-20   49  TELEMARKETING BOX#110    ENTERED (QUESTION)
 1:01:25PM10-20   50  MESSAGE DISTRIBUTED TO 22607202
 1:05:50PM10-20   51  TELEMARKETING BOX#100    ENTERED (HELLO)
 1:05:55PM10-20   52  TELEMARKETING BOX#110    ENTERED (QUESTION)
 1:06:04PM10-20   53  TELEMARKETING BOX#130    ENTERED (GOODBYE)
 1:06:06PM10-20   54  MESSAGE DISTRIBUTED TO 22605052
 1:11:59PM10-20   55  TELEMARKETING BOX#100    ENTERED (HELLO)
 1:12:04PM10-20   56  TELEMARKETING BOX#110    ENTERED (QUESTION)
 1:12:13PM10-20   57  TELEMARKETING BOX#130    ENTERED (GOODBYE)
 1:12:15PM10-20   58  MESSAGE DISTRIBUTED TO 22607559
 1:13:28PM10-20   59  TELEMARKETING BOX#100    ENTERED (HELLO)
 1:13:32PM10-20   60  TELEMARKETING BOX#110    ENTERED (QUESTION)
 1:13:40PM10-20   61  MESSAGE DISTRIBUTED TO 22568277
 1:41:12PM10-20    4  TELEMARKETING BOX#100    ENTERED (HELLO)
 1:41:19PM10-20    5  TELEMARKETING BOX#110    ENTERED (QUESTION)
 1:41:31PM10-20    6 *MESSAGE  A022 LEFT  BOX#110    T= 00:03
 1:41:31PM10-20    7  TELEMARKETING BOX#130    ENTERED (GOODBYE)
 1:41:33PM10-20    8  MESSAGE DISTRIBUTED TO 22604054
 2:01:40PM10-20    4  TELEMARKETING BOX#100    ENTERED (HELLO)
 2:01:46PM10-20    5  TELEMARKETING BOX#110    ENTERED (QUESTION)
 2:02:13PM10-20    6 *MESSAGE  A023 LEFT  BOX#110    T= 00:17
 2:02:13PM10-20    7  TELEMARKETING BOX#130    ENTERED (GOODBYE)
 2:02:15PM10-20    8  MESSAGE DISTRIBUTED TO 22604054
 2:07:56PM10-20    4  TELEMARKETING BOX#100    ENTERED (HELLO)
 2:08:02PM10-20    5  TELEMARKETING BOX#110    ENTERED (QUESTION)
 2:08:13PM10-20    6  MESSAGE DISTRIBUTED TO 22604054
 2:14:35PM10-20    7  TELEMARKETING BOX#100    ENTERED (HELLO)
 2:14:41PM10-20    8  TELEMARKETING BOX#110    ENTERED (QUESTION)
 2:15:08PM10-20    9 *MESSAGE  A024 LEFT  BOX#110    T= 00:17
 2:15:08PM10-20   10  TELEMARKETING BOX#130    ENTERED (GOODBYE)
 2:15:10PM10-20   11  MESSAGE DISTRIBUTED TO 22569637
 2:15:38PM10-20   12  DISTRIBUTION COMPLETED
 2:26:38PM10-20    4  TELEMARKETING BOX#100    ENTERED (HELLO)
 2:26:44PM10-20    5  TELEMARKETING BOX#110    ENTERED (QUESTION)
 2:26:55PM10-20    6  MESSAGE DISTRIBUTED TO 22600505
 2:27:22PM10-20    7  TELEMARKETING BOX#100    ENTERED (HELLO)
 2:27:29PM10-20    8  TELEMARKETING BOX#110    ENTERED (QUESTION)
 2:27:48PM10-20    9 *MESSAGE  A025 LEFT  BOX#110    T= 00:10
 2:27:48PM10-20   10  TELEMARKETING BOX#130    ENTERED (GOODBYE)
 2:27:49PM10-20   11  MESSAGE DISTRIBUTED TO 22567840
 2:28:06PM10-20   12  TELEMARKETING BOX#100    ENTERED (HELLO)
 2:28:13PM10-20   13  TELEMARKETING BOX#110    ENTERED (QUESTION)
 2:28:23PM10-20   14  MESSAGE DISTRIBUTED TO 22600505
 2:30:15PM10-20   15  TELEMARKETING BOX#100    ENTERED (HELLO)
 2:30:21PM10-20   16  TELEMARKETING BOX#110    ENTERED (QUESTION)
 2:30:32PM10-20   17  MESSAGE DISTRIBUTED TO 22567840
 2:30:54PM10-20   18  TELEMARKETING BOX#100    ENTERED (HELLO)
 2:31:01PM10-20   19  TELEMARKETING BOX#110    ENTERED (QUESTION)
 2:31:14PM10-20   20 *MESSAGE  A026 LEFT  BOX#110    T= 00:04
 2:31:14PM10-20   21  TELEMARKETING BOX#130    ENTERED (GOODBYE)
 2:31:16PM10-20   22  MESSAGE DISTRIBUTED TO 22600505
 2:34:10PM10-20   23  TELEMARKETING BOX#100    ENTERED (HELLO)
 2:34:17PM10-20   24  TELEMARKETING BOX#110    ENTERED (QUESTION)
 2:34:46PM10-20   25 *MESSAGE  A027 LEFT  BOX#110    T= 00:20
 2:34:47PM10-20   26  TELEMARKETING BOX#130    ENTERED (GOODBYE)
 2:34:48PM10-20   27  MESSAGE DISTRIBUTED TO 22568277
 2:34:59PM10-20   28  TELEMARKETING BOX#100    ENTERED (HELLO)
 2:35:06PM10-20   29  TELEMARKETING BOX#110    ENTERED (QUESTION)
 2:35:29PM10-20   30 *MESSAGE  A028 LEFT  BOX#110    T= 00:14
 2:35:29PM10-20   31  TELEMARKETING BOX#130    ENTERED (GOODBYE)
 2:35:31PM10-20   32  MESSAGE DISTRIBUTED TO 22568277
 2:35:43PM10-20   33  TELEMARKETING BOX#100    ENTERED (HELLO)
 2:35:49PM10-20   34  TELEMARKETING BOX#110    ENTERED (QUESTION)
 2:36:10PM10-20   35 *MESSAGE  A029 LEFT  BOX#110    T= 00:12
 2:36:10PM10-20   36  TELEMARKETING BOX#130    ENTERED (GOODBYE)
 2:36:12PM10-20   37  MESSAGE DISTRIBUTED TO 22568277
 2:36:56PM10-20   38  TELEMARKETING BOX#100    ENTERED (HELLO)
 2:37:03PM10-20   39  TELEMARKETING BOX#110    ENTERED (QUESTION)
 2:37:27PM10-20   40 *MESSAGE  A030 LEFT  BOX#110    T= 00:15
 2:37:27PM10-20   41  TELEMARKETING BOX#130    ENTERED (GOODBYE)
 2:37:29PM10-20   42  MESSAGE DISTRIBUTED TO 22567840
 2:37:32PM10-20   43  DISTRIBUTION COMPLETED
 2:48:41PM10-20    4  TELEMARKETING BOX#100    ENTERED (HELLO)
 2:48:47PM10-20    5  TELEMARKETING BOX#110    ENTERED (QUESTION)
 2:48:58PM10-20    6  MESSAGE DISTRIBUTED TO 22604054
 2:56:21PM10-20    4  TELEMARKETING BOX#100    ENTERED (HELLO)
 2:56:28PM10-20    5  TELEMARKETING BOX#110    ENTERED (QUESTION)
 2:56:44PM10-20    6 *MESSAGE  A031 LEFT  BOX#110    T= 00:07
 2:56:44PM10-20    7  TELEMARKETING BOX#130    ENTERED (GOODBYE)
 2:56:46PM10-20    8  MESSAGE DISTRIBUTED TO 22603589
 3:05:33PM10-20    9  TELEMARKETING BOX#100    ENTERED (HELLO)
 3:05:40PM10-20   10  TELEMARKETING BOX#110    ENTERED (QUESTION)
 3:05:50PM10-20   11  MESSAGE DISTRIBUTED TO 22567204
 3:06:15PM10-20   12  TELEMARKETING BOX#100    ENTERED (HELLO)
 3:06:21PM10-20   13  TELEMARKETING BOX#110    ENTERED (QUESTION)
 3:06:40PM10-20   14 *MESSAGE  A032 LEFT  BOX#110    T= 00:09
 3:06:40PM10-20   15  TELEMARKETING BOX#130    ENTERED (GOODBYE)
 3:06:42PM10-20   16  MESSAGE DISTRIBUTED TO 22569427
 3:07:04PM10-20   17  TELEMARKETING BOX#100    ENTERED (HELLO)
```

Photo KLM Aerocarto - Arnhem, Holland

THE BIJLMER GROUP PROVIDED SLOGANS AND IMAGES FOR LOW-TECH DISPLAY IN LOCAL AREAS.

1. EXPERIMENT FEEDBACK CARDS; 2. CAMERA; 3. SLIDE FILM; 4. SLIDE MOUNTS; 5. COMPUTER AND MONITOR; 6. FLAT-BED SCANNER; 7. COMPUTER PRINTER; 8. SLOGAN SUGGESTION BOOKLET; 9. SLOGANBOARD RAIL; 10. METAL RINGS FOR RAIL; 11. HOLE PUNCHES; 12. CARD FOR SLOGANBOARDS; 13. SLIDE PROJECTOR; 14. PROJECTION SCREEN; 15. SPRAY GLUE

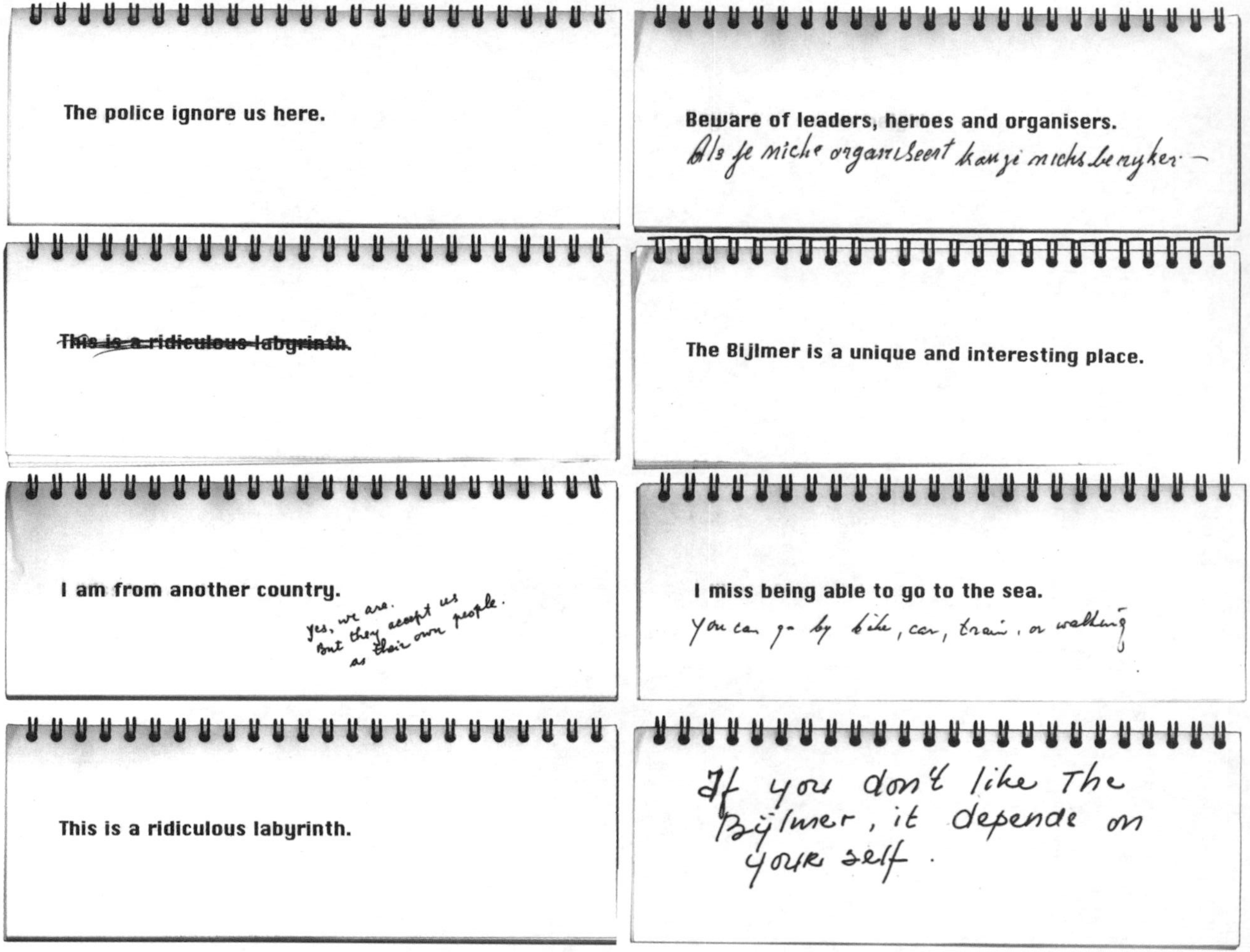

Beware of leaders, heroes and organisers.

Als je niche organiseent kanje michslenyker. —

The Bijlmer is a unique and interesting place.

I miss being able to go to the sea.

You can go by bike, car, train, or walking.

The police ignore us here.

~~This is a ridiculous labyrinth.~~

I am from another country.

yes, we are. we accept us
but they own people.
as

This is a ridiculous labyrinth.

If you don't like the
Bijlmer, it depende on
your self.

160

Don't destroy our Bijlmermeer.

The Bijlmer Test

Performing tests of the proposals in Oslo, Peccioli, and the Bijlmer took a surprising amount of time, despite the technological simplicity of the experimental situations we created. Clearly, implementing more technically sophisticated prototypes of all three systems would be impossible. We settled with little difficulty on developing and testing the Projected Realities system for the Bijlmer. In part, this was because our experiment had worked best there, with few obvious technical or conceptual problems and an enthusiastic response from the local inhabitants. More than this, however, we were intrigued by the complexity of this area and wanted to explore further the ideas it had inspired.

By this time we had a fairly clear idea of how the Projected Realities system might work. But we had left open almost all design decisions about the forms that particular elements in the system should take. This had been a deliberate decision: in developing the proposal, we had been primarily concerned with drawing our partners into a shared imaginary world, and so avoided unnecessarily distracting design details. Instead, we provided a 'catalogue of parts' with the proposal, a series of simple diagrams with suggestive labels that served as props for imagining the system that might eventually be built. The catalogue we created for the Bijlmer was an important starting point as we discussed how to develop the system further.

Another starting point came from the experiment we had done earlier. We believed that its success was not in spite of the modest materials we had used – originally chosen for affordability and to communicate the components' provisional nature – but because of them. Employing materials and methods that inhabitants could imagine using themselves removed the test pieces from product genres associated with advertising or government, making them accessible for ownership, use and adaptation. We wanted to maintain this accessibility in our final designs, but also to create potentially enduring pieces of street furniture which would communicate electronically.

FOCUSING THE DESIGN / We had proposed four main components for the Bijlmer system: scanning devices to collect images and slogans from the older people, a mains radio system to collect and integrate individual attitudes from people in their flats, and slogan furniture and image boards for public display. These would link together to allow people to express their attitudes to an increasingly larger public. We had tested the functions of the two most visible of these elements, the slogan and image displays, and found they worked well. Now we needed to flesh out the design of a more complete working system.

The final version of the system coalesced slowly as we discussed many small issues and made decisions over time. We discuss some of these issues here, but we are aware that, by organising them, the process may appear more logical than it actually was. In reality, any linear refinement and problem solving were deeply enmeshed in a process that we experienced as simultaneous and intuitive.

We decided at the outset to focus on collecting and displaying images and slogans from the older people, rather than developing special scanning devices. The role we were suggesting seemed more important than the specific devices they might use.

Developing a working mains radio system seemed too complicated for a short test. We decided to reuse the telemarketing system we had originally tried in Oslo, asking people to choose images from a printed 'menu' they could keep near their phones.

We rejected LED text displays for slogan furniture early in the process because of their associations with commercial systems and resulting impersonality. From the alternatives we discussed, scrolling devices had the appeal of being electronically controllable while maintaining ties with mechanical objects. They also allowed slogans to be handwritten. While these might be difficult to read, they would retain a personality and individuality lost through print.

Slogan displays might be shown on their own, but associating them with public benches seemed to give them a more social context. If text displays were mounted high overhead, they could be seen by many people and remain associated with a bench user. They might seem functionally separate from the furniture, however, and appear too monumental. We began to enjoy the idea that sitting on the benches might obscure the slogans. It would add an interesting tension to the pieces: would they be signs, or furniture? Perhaps people sitting on the benches would be perceived as owning the slogans.

Displaying images on large-scale LCD displays or video walls seemed too inaccessible and suggestive of advertising, in part because of their high cost. We thought about using large scrolls printed with images for the displays, but decided to explore other options. For instance, parasite displays, showing small images or slogans, might be mounted on light poles or signposts. The idea of building on the public infrastructure in this way was appealing. But we returned to larger image displays that many people could see, realising that using a linear bank of monitors would allow segments of large images to be shown, and that as the images moved, people would integrate them over time.

Finally, we considered a variety of ways that the system components might communicate – SMS messages, infrared, even wires. In the end we realised that dial tones sent over CB radio channels would be robust, affordable, and easy to develop.

As our design considerations gelled, an outline of the final prototype system emerged:

-- Images and slogans would be collected with the help of the older people, who would be asked to rate each along a number of dimensions to capture emotional content.
-- Volunteers would be given printed menus of images identified by numbers. The telemarketing system would call them periodically, prompting them to enter the number of a preferred image.
-- A central server, controlling the telemarketing system, would combine ratings corresponding to chosen images and map the result to an appropriate slogan.
-- Slogans would be shown on scrolls built into the back of benches. DTMF codes sent via CB radio would allow the server to change them. Slogans could also be changed manually by passers-by.
-- Imagebanks using a number of large televisions arranged linearly would show segments of images on the outskirts of the Bijlmer.
-- The images would be determined by the server, which would poll the Sloganbenches and map the attitudes they revealed to an appropriate image.

Having outlined the basic system design, we started refining our sketches of the forms the Sloganbenches and Imagebank would take. A series of drawings, diagrams, and models – including full-scale cardboard models for test outdoors – was used to develop the design of the pieces, while on-screen animations were used to explore how the images might appear over time.

The forms of the Sloganbenches and Imagebank were kept simple and functional, like three-dimensional diagrams, to indicate that the pieces were components of a system that was still incompletely developed. While we wanted the objects to appear intriguing, we were satisfied that this would emerge naturally from their conceptual uniqueness. For instance, the use of wood-grain laminate as a finish for both the Sloganbenches and the Imagebank came from the desire to associate the pieces with domestic furniture. The intention was to emphasise their function of giving access to the Bijlmer's interior spaces.

The final prototypes – three Sloganbenches and an Imagebank – were constructed from laminated MDF over steel frames. Using sheet metal for the fabric of the objects, though appropriate for permanent street furniture, was prohibitively expensive. As these were intended to be test pieces, we settled for the less costly construction – little appreciating the implications of having to shelter them from the elements every evening.

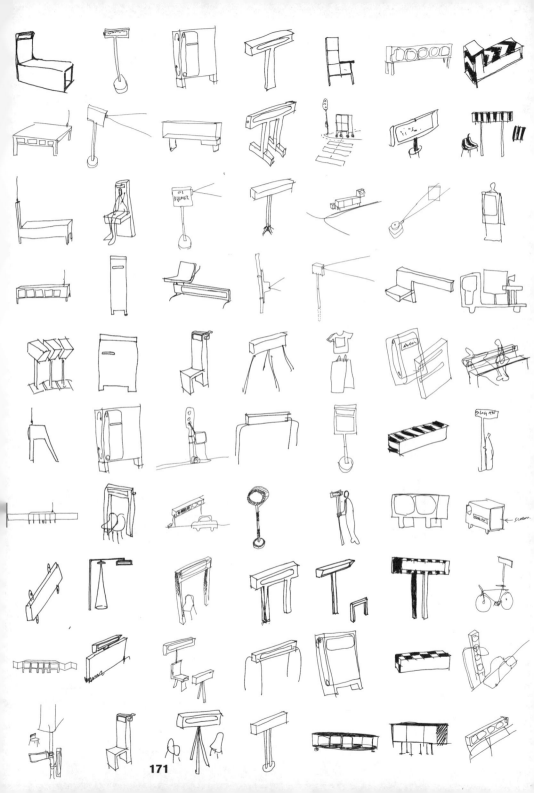

AN OVERVIEW OF THE SYSTEM

A Bijlmermeer Central Server flat
  A1 400MHz PC with Bigmouth
    hard&software
  A2 Macintosh G3 computer running
    Director programme
  A3 Regulated 12v power supply
  A4 Stamp and DTMF chips
  A5 Danita 1240 CEPT CB radio
  A6 CB aerial
B Image Bank
C Slogan Bench
D Home telephones

1 DTMF (Touch Tone) dialogue over tel
  phone line
2 DTMF (Touch Tone) dialogue over CB
  CEPT channel 19
3 Mains electricity
4 Local telephone line in
5 Base 10 cross over cable
6 Serial port cable
7 Data transfer and radio switching
8 50ohm coaxial cable
9 Mains power 240vAC
10 12vDC

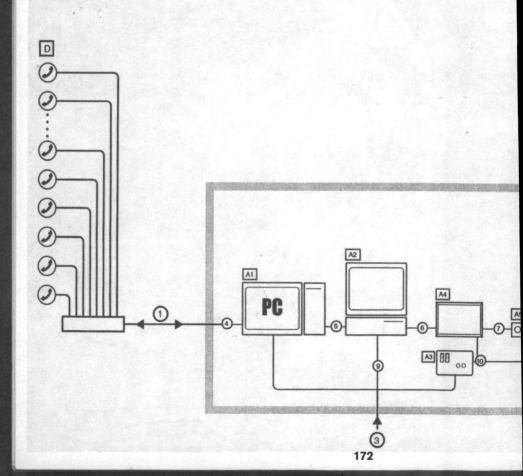

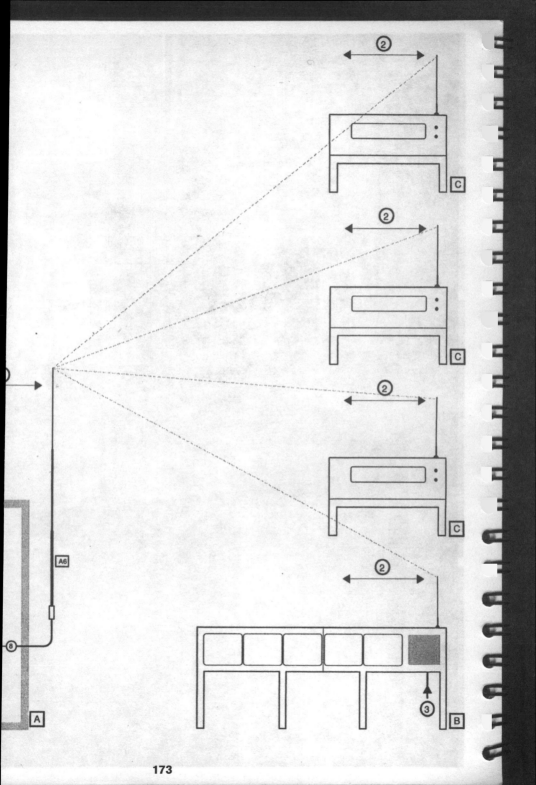

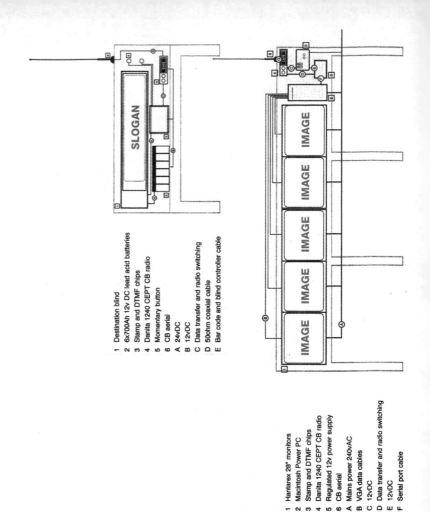

1 Destination blind
2 6x700Ah 12v DC lead acid batteries
3 Stamp and DTMF chips
4 Danita 1240 CEPT CB radio
5 Momentary button
6 CB aerial
A 24vDC
B 12vDC
C Data transfer and radio switching
D 50ohm coaxial cable
E Bar code and blind controller cable

1 Hantarex 28" monitors
2 Macintosh Power PC
3 Stamp and DTMF chips
4 Danita 1240 CEPT CB radio
5 Regulated 12v power supply
6 CB aerial
A Mains power 240vAC
B VGA data cables
C 12vDC
D Data transfer and radio switching
E 12vDC
F Serial port cable

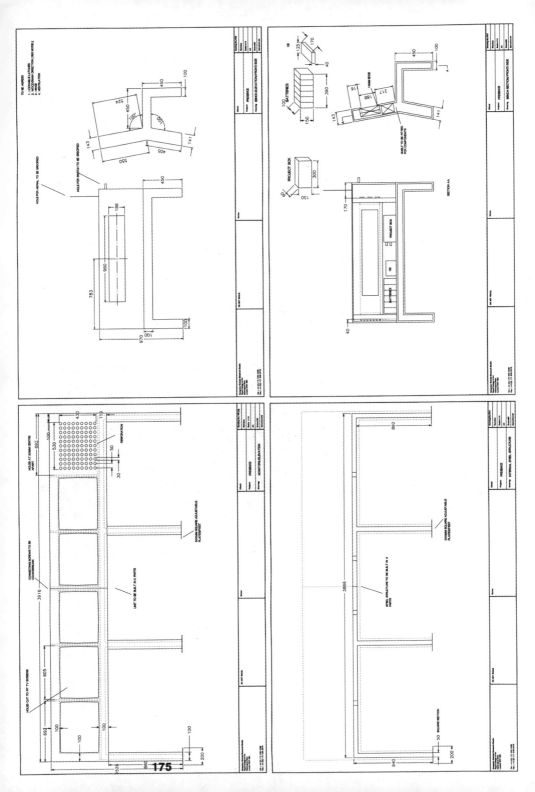

175

FINAL PROTOTYPES OF THE SLOGANBENCH AND IMAGEBANK.

PREPARATIONS / About halfway through this process, two members of the team visited the Bijlmer to find potential sites for the objects and meet with local government officials. Walks along the nearby motorways made it clear that deploying the Imagebank along them would be ineffective due to their scale and the high speed of the traffic. The focus shifted to intersections on the borders of the Bijlmer. Four sites were chosen and discussed with the older people. Three were rejected as having inappropriate traffic (too local, or too wealthy). One was highlighted by the older people as particularly appropriate, with a suitably wide verge and traffic from both the inside and outside of the Bijlmer. The local authorities were informed about the project, and permission given to deploy the pieces in the public areas of the Bijlmer.

A second visit was made about a month before the deployment of the prototypes, to collect images and slogans from the older people. Many images had already been gathered by the older people, using disposable cameras distributed by the local site researcher. They also brought in their own photographs, newspapers, and other items. Using a digital scanner, we captured these images, as well as scans of their hands and things they were carrying with them. Between these sources, we collected a large number of images from which we eventually chose 100 for use with the prototypes.

The older people also generated new slogans during this visit, prompted by the slogans used in the earlier experiment. This allowed consideration of some of the strengths and weaknesses of the former slogans, which had seemed too easily to be read as advertising, or as political or religious. The new slogans produced by the group seemed to avoid these problems while revealing facets of the group's attitudes.

Finally, we asked the older people to rate each of the images and slogans along three dimensions inspired by semantic differentials (a classic approach to measuring meaning in psycholinguistics). These provided numerical representations for each of the items that could be used to map them together algorithmically. We had developed the scales through informal tests in which we used various dimensions (e.g. 'positive-negative', 'self-other') to rate images and slogans, and map them together using a simple algorithm based loosely on neural net processing. The older people found the scales fairly difficult to use, and we had to help them adjust some of their ratings as we collected the materials. With better design of the input, however – for instance, specialised scanning devices equipped with dials for indicating meaning – such scales would probably work fairly well. In any case, the intention was not to produce 'correct' mappings, but ones that were meaningful enough to be evocative.

Cartography: Geo-informatie Amsterdam

TESTING THE PROTOTYPES /

After taking delivery of the benches and Imagebank, fitting them with the electronic components, and testing the system, we transported the equipment to the Netherlands in a transit van. The telemarketing system, slogan- and image-server, and CB equipment were all set up in a borrowed flat high in one of the large housing block.

We met again with the group of older people to transfer slogans to the fabric scrolls. This also provided a chance to modify the slogans generated during the previous visit, and to create new ones.

Finally, we revisited the sites with our local coordinator. We learned that the site we had agreed for the Imagebank had later been modified by the police to avoid creating a traffic hazard. This raised two problems: the new site was difficult to see properly from a moving automobile, and an electrical generator would have to be used because the site was too far from the nearest building to run a power line. Despite our negotiations over the next days, we were unable to resolve these problems satisfactorily.

In their initial presentation, the Sloganbenches were placed along a well-used public path, near green parkland, large housing blocks, and a local mosque. The Imagebank was set up temporarily behind the social centre in which we met the older people, oriented so it could be seen from within the centre. The pieces were visited by the older people, local press, and other interested designers and researchers, as well as local residents and passers-by.

Over subsequent days, we moved the Sloganbenches to another nearby pathway to protect them from inclement weather. Sheltered by overhead rail tracks, the path ran between a collection of housing blocks and the local shopping arcade. Again it was a well-frequented area, and many people of all ages stopped to interact with the benches and discuss the project.

The telemarketing system was tested on local volunteers who were given booklets of images to take home. When the system called them, they were asked to enter the number of the image that they found most representative of their current attitude.

Due to continuing difficulties with sourcing electricity and obtaining permission for a suitable roadside site, we decided to test the Imagebank separately inside and outside the Bijlmer. In the Bijlmer, we tested the Imagebank in a space linking the shopping arcade with a local train stop. The advantage of this site was that it was easy to discuss the piece with local inhabitants, which would have been difficult by a roadside.

On the last day of the trial, we moved the Imagebank to the Netherlands Design Institute to better understand how the images would be received by outsiders to the Bijlmer. Upon the Institute's request, we left both the Imagebank and a Sloganbench behind for them to show to visitors for their feedback.

Schedule A
Equipment Travelling to Netherlands Design Institute

Qty	Description	Est Value per item	Total Est Value
3	Wooden Benches	£900 each	£2100
3	Destination Blinds	£600 each	£1800
5	Aerial	4@£30, 1@£60	£ 180
3	Battery Pack	£50 each	£ 150
1	Battery Charger	£40 each	£ 40
5	Project Boxes	£200 each	£ 200
5	CB Radios	£50 each	£ 250
5	28" TV's	£1000 each	£5000
1	Furniture in 4 parts	£2500	£2500
1	G3 Computer	£1600	£1600
1	9600 Mac Computer	£1400	£1400
1	G3 Laptop	£2000	£2000
1	PC	£1400	£1400
1	Telephone	£7	£ 7
1	Mini Speaker	£10	£ 10
1	Toolbox	£300	£ 300
?	Miscellaneous Cables	£200	£ 200
1	Box of Blinds	£200	£ 200
3	Personal Luggage	£200 each	£ 600
1	Box of General Paperwork	£200	£ 200
1	Digital Camera	£800	£ 800
1	Crimpt Tool Kit	£30	£ 30

Total Estimated Value   **£20,967**

28.5.99

Royal College of Art
Postgraduate Art & Design

Kensington Gore
London SW7 2EU
Telephone 0171 590 4444
Fax 0171 590 4500

To Whom It May Concern:

To Whom It May Concern

This is to confirm that Shona Kitchen, Ben Hooker and Brendan Walker are all Researchers at the Royal College of Art in the Computer Related Design Department.

They are travelling to Amsterdam to the Netherlands Design Institute (Kaisergracht 609, 1017 DS) to conduct research. They will be returning on 5th June 1999.

They are transporting equipment with them, which is outlined in Schedule A. All of this equipment will be returning with them.

Yours Faithfully

Bill Gaver
Computer Related Design Department
Royal College of Art

School of
Art

School of
Architecture
& Design

School of
Communications

School of
Fashion
& Textiles

School of
Fine Art

School of
Humanities

WHAT WE LEARNED / The test of the Projected Realities prototypes was encouraging both for us and the local populace, indicating that the system could be further developed. Both the older people and general inhabitants were intrigued by, and positive about, the individual objects and the overall system concept.

The older people participated enthusiastically in gathering slogans and images for the tests of the system. Having been told about the plans for the Sloganbenches and image boards, they readily spent time taking pictures of the area, brought us their own pictures and objects to scan, and allowed us to scan their hands and things they carried with them. In addition, they were willing to devote their efforts to authoring slogans, and changed their approach at our suggestion, when initial slogans seemed too promotional, religious, or political to be effective. Finally, they were happy to write the slogans by hand on the scrolls, despite this being a rather time-consuming process (which we would expect to become much quicker as they learned to relax and not labour unduly over the quality of their writing).

The enjoyment found by the older people in participating in our tests was encouraging for the prospects of a longer-term, self-sustaining version of the Projected Realities system. The fact that they were willing to provide slogans and images on three separate occasions (the earlier experiment, the preliminary visit, and the initial phases of this test) indicates that their enthusiasm might be maintained over a longer period of time. However, our involvement was probably an important factor in their interest. If the Projected Realities system were to be developed for long-term deployment, it would probably be useful to involve outside facilitators in its continued running – particularly artists, social commentators, or politicians interested in exploring specific issues via the publicly-displayed slogans and images.

Local inhabitants also reacted positively to the experiment. The Sloganbenches, in particular, gained a great deal of attention. During our tests, many passers-by paused at the benches, reading and discussing the slogans, exploring the range of statements to be found, and engaging us in conversations about the project. In discussions, people were unanimous in their support of the Projected Realities system, and only protested when they learned that the furniture was a part of a test, rather than a permanent addition to the area.

The Sloganbenches proved to be particularly appealing to children, which we had not expected. Seemingly attracted by their unusual appearance and the opportunities for interaction afforded by the benches, children were drawn into discussions about the slogans with each other, their parents, and others. In this way, the benches became a medium for communication between the older people and children, a potential that might be expanded in future development.

A key to the success of the Sloganbenches, we believe, is in the balance they found between the familiar and the strange. As benches they were immediately recognised and accepted – and in fact used, with people sitting on them to eat their lunches, rest, or discuss the slogans. But because of their unusual forms and materials, and particularly the slogans embedded in their backs, they intrigued people. While the slogans themselves were immediately comprehensible both in content and in their form as a sort of graffiti, the intentions behind them and the identity of their authors were less clear. This balance between familiarity and strangeness, it seems, allowed the Sloganbenches to draw people into an increasingly intense engagement, with curiosity fuelling thought about the project and the particular statements.

Balancing familiarity and strangeness also seemed successful for the Imagebank. The scale was large enough to be seen from a good distance even in outdoor spaces (where the apparent size of objects seems to rapidly diminish), yet it did not appear as a kind of monumental display, a spectacle that only the government or a commercial agency could afford.

The images, too, mixed the ordinary with the unusual. Most of the pictures showed everyday life in and around the Bijlmer, with their very mundanity a source of interest. Showing only a long strip through the images, though, seemed to allow a fresh view, preventing them from seeming like an out-of-place slide show (a problem for the earlier experiment). Juxtaposing different images to indicate mixed attitudes helped, allowing unexpected resonances to form between the various pictures.

While the Projected Realities test was successful on the whole, we also encountered – and learned from – many problems.

For instance, the Imagebank worked well in our tests, but we were disappointed not to be able to try it near a public roadway as we had intended. A primary lesson from this is the difficulty of producing these sorts of public designs, particularly in different countries. Our local partners, the government, and police were extremely helpful in establishing a possible location for siting the Imagebank, but this was ultimately undone by problems in details: the site was too far from a stoplight for drivers to have a chance to view it properly; it was facing the sun which would wash out the images; and supplying power was difficult. The latter two issues are relatively minor and could be overcome easily (though not, in the event, quickly enough for our experiment). Conflicts between viewing the Imagebank and traffic safety, on the other hand, appear more difficult to solve, even with our plan to 'turn off' the Imagebank when lights were green.

If the Projected Realities system were to be taken forward, then, alternative ways to allow outsiders to view the images would need to be explored. Showing the Imagebank in Amsterdam inside a building suggested a gallery experience which undermined its intention as a design for public communication. Local metro stations, on the other hand, are promising in meeting the myriad demands for successful placement, combining the advantages of roadside and gallery displays. Alternatively, ideas for 'parasitical' displays could be revisited, with smaller versions populating the pathways and roadsides outside the central area of the Bijlmer.

Using the telemarketing system to poll people's image choices at home was similarly problematic, being technically but not socially successful. During the time of our trials, we received a number of answers indicating that participants could use the system and make sense of the task. A number of difficulties arose, however. First, a large proportion of Bijlmer inhabitants carried mobile phones rather than using land lines. While this didn't prevent their participation – several people agreed to carry the image booklets with them – it clearly changed the nature of the system. Probably related to this, we had problems finding people to join the experiment. While we had requested that the local researcher try to find about fifty people to participate, only a few had been found on our arrival. More signed up over conversations about the Sloganbenches and Imagebank, but too late for the trials to be run as envisioned.

Using the telemarketing system to perform automated polling was only a weak approximation of the original mains radio concept, requiring more intensive preparation to make it work. The key difference is in the balance of effort and payoffs required of users to register attitudes in the two systems. Polling is intrusive, requiring that people be interrupted and asked to consciously choose an image. The mains radio devices, on the other hand, registered attitudes as a peripheral side effect of a more inviting activity – choosing images for display in the home.

While testing the original mains radio concept was impossible at this stage, such success as we had even with the intrusive telemarketing solution does suggest the concept could work. People did find the task meaningful and were interested in the booklets of images. The weaknesses, then, seemed due to the telemarketing approximation, rather than the concept itself. If offered devices that would add value in their everyday lives – allowing them to display interesting images in their homes – we expect many more people would want to take part in the system.

(FOLLOWING PAGES) TESTING THE PROJECTIVE REALITIES SYSTEM OVER A WEEK-LONG PERIOD IN THE BIJLMER.

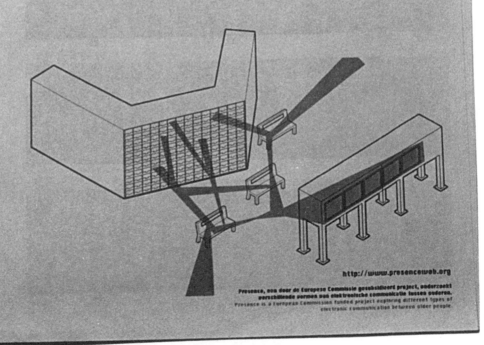

http://www.presenceweb.org

Presence, een door de Europese Commissie gesubsidieerd project, onderzoekt
verschillende vormen van elektronische communicatie tussen ouderen.
Presence is a European Commission funded project exploring different types of
electronic communication between older people.

185

186

X

THE TREES THE BIRDS THEY
MAKE ME FEEL HAPPY

IK BEN BANG

I AM DIVORCED RETIRED LIKE
MUSIC AND A DRINK

EERST WAS DE FAZANTENHOF VO
L MET DRUGS   NU GAATT BETER

THE SUN IS SHINING FOR
EVERYBODY

I AM AT PEACE WITH THE
WORLD

I MISS BEING ABLE TO GO TO
THE SEA

I AM FROM ANOTHER COUNTRY
CAN YOU SEE IT?

WE FEEL HAPPY IN THE BIJLMER
EVERYBODY IS IMPORTANT

NOS ANTIANO TIN NOS CULTURA

VUIL IN DE CONTAINER NIET
ER NAAST

VOOR DE VRIJHEID HEBBEN WIJ
DE VRIJHEIDS-OORLOG NODIG!

LAAT JE BUREN NIET MET JE
MUZIEK MEEGENIETEN

DE BIJLMER IS MIJN TWEEDE
THUIS

METHADON JAINIET VOOR DE
OGEN VAN KINDEREN

IK TRACHT ME IN EEN ANDER
ZIJN SITUATIE TE PLAATSEN

I USED TO BE RESTLESS BECAU
SE OF NEGATIVE THOUGHTS

X

193

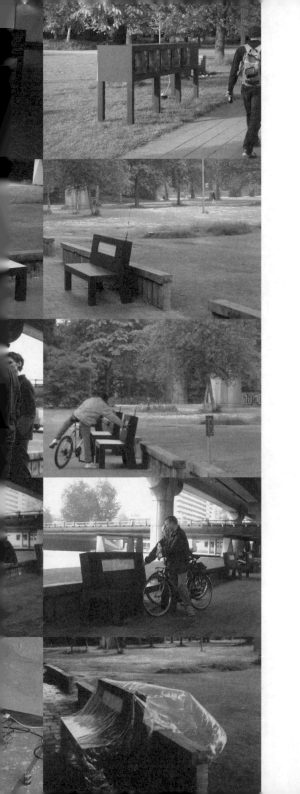

ACCOUNTABILITY

Science is epistemologically accountable. In pursuing its goal of producing causal explanations of the world, what distinguishes science from similar endeavours (e.g. religion) is that the methods employed to establish facts, construct theories, and relate the two are used to justify the validity of one's work, not the results of these methods. No matter how plausible or desirable a statement or theory, it does not count as science unless the basis for asserting it is clear and verifiable. Conversely, no matter how implausible or even dangerous a statement ('the earth revolves around the sun'), it is a scientific fact if the means used to assert it are sound. In principle, epistemological accountability allows science to establish causal models that are counter to prevailing opinion, thus defending progress against prejudice. But epistemological accountability also implies that work can be scientifically valid despite being obvious or trivial. The essential question in examining a scientific statement is not 'does this seem interesting/useful/inspiring', but 'how do you know what you say is true?'

A number of extra-scientific factors can influence the ways that science actually gets done. Scientists, like anyone, have intuitions, aesthetic reactions, desires, and ethical beliefs. These have important influences on the facts and hypotheses that are pursued, either by individuals (e.g. the influence of visual analogies such as snakes or spiral staircases) or by society (e.g. unfashionable subjects may not be published or funded, while those of importance to special interest groups are highly supported). But these ways of knowing only play an indirect role in scientific investigations. Scientific explanations tend to be valued insofar as they generalise beyond particular circumstances or observers, leading to new predictions or understandings. But within the scientific peer review system, questions of methodological soundness are the primary grounds for accepting or rejecting work.

There are several implications of science's foundation on epistemological accountability. First, scientific methods must be articulated and precise. These methods – controlled empirical investigations, statistical analyses, logic and deduction – allow the chains of inference used to posit facts or theories to be examined and verified by independent researchers. Second, facts are, by definition, objective and replicable. That is, they do not depend on any given person's perception or beliefs, and will be found in a given set of circumstances by anybody who does the looking and whenever they look.

Science's methodological requirements place constraints on the sorts of investigations that can be pursued. Subjective ways of knowing the world are not only out of bounds in scientific methodology, but are also difficult to address as the content of scientific studies. The need for articulation, objectivity, and generality means that a great deal of human experience can only be studied from the outside, if at all. Replicable measures of emotions, influences, insights, etc., often seem to miss subtleties of experiencing the phenomena themselves. Scientists know much that they cannot say, and which cannot be said within the scientific discourse.

Design is aesthetically accountable. The question is whether a design 'works,' not whether the methods used to devise them are sound. 'Working' can mean many things – from actually functioning as intended, to embodying a desirable aesthetic, to conveying appropriate social and cultural messages. Primarily, however, 'working' refers to the integration and balance of all these factors, the degree to which they are addressed with elegance and appeal to their audience. This is an aesthetic judgement in the widest sense of the term, referring not just to the aesthetics of form, but to the aesthetics of interaction, of use and of ideas. It may be informed by analysis, but insofar as it addresses the totality of a design, it is not itself analytic but synthetic.

Design is not epistemologically accountable; designers do not have to justify their methods as scientists do. There are three reasons for this. First, the goal of design is to produce artefacts, systems, and processes, and not, primarily, causal explanations. Second, successful designs depend on the synthesis of many different factors, ranging from the functions they provide, to their aesthetics, to the economics of their manufacture. Analytical understandings of many of these factors, and of their synthesis itself, may be intractable – and even if they are possible, it is unnecessary and perhaps inefficient for designers to achieve them. Finally, the products of design are usually meant for people other than the designer, and their success is often mediated by the marketplace. Justifications of design in terms of the methods used to create them are largely irrelevant in this context. Products based on explicit and accountable methods may fail; conversely, successful products may be based on methods that appear confused, misguided, or at least unarticulated.

If designers are not accountable for the methods they use, and do not need to articulate the myriad of design decisions they integrate, designs nonetheless 'speak for themselves'. Designs can be seen as embodiments of beliefs or theories about the myriad of issues relevant to them. These beliefs need not be explicated by the designer, and indeed may not have been the result of conscious choice. But in embodying beliefs and theories in an integrated design, designers can be seen as researchers, asserting hypotheses and theories that will be tested aesthetically rather than empirically.

The ability to test ideas articulated through design rather than words, and evaluate them aesthetically rather than logically, allows designers to approach topics that seem inaccessible to science – topics such as aesthetic pleasure on the one hand, and cultural implications on the other. Moreover, these things can be approached idiosyncratically without losing importance or validity. Subjectivity can be mined in the hope of finding universality by virtue of a concordance of individual responses; science can be used as inspiration, as can the popular press, anecdotes, or daydreams. The results may not be constrained by logical necessity, but they are subject to the collective subjectivity of the community which evaluates them. Designers, like scientists, know much that they cannot say. But unlike scientists, their goal is to express their knowledge through design itself.

Completion

The Bijlmer trial marked the conclusion of the Presence project. At the end of the week we packed the rental van with the benches, the Imagebank, our computers, CB equipment and other gear, and returned to London. After writing the final report and attending the review meeting, putting the pieces in storage and archiving the materials we had collected, we turned our attention to other projects. Presence was over.

We did consider various ways to continue the project. A museum in the Bijlmer expressed interest in the system, as did a community group in south London. Public money might have been available to redeploy it in these contexts, or perhaps even to develop the furniture in a more permanent form.

It was clear, however, that we would want to redesign the system before deploying it in other settings. In a museum environment it would be difficult to achieve the community ownership we were advocating, but in other communities the social components of the system – meetings with older people, input from local participants, the appropriate materials to display – would all have to be rethought. Even the form of the elements, the benches and the Imagebank, would only work in certain kinds of environment.

In the end, therefore, we decided against pursuing the Projected Realities system further. While we believe that it could be extended to other contexts, we had learned most of what we wanted to learn. Rather than trying to develop and maintain the Projected Realities system itself, we decided to carry the lessons it had taught to new projects and new contexts. Thus while elements of the system have been exhibited in various ways, they serve as an archive of the project, rather than a living embodiment of Projected Realities.

LEAVING THE BIJLMER / The experiment also marked the end of our relationship with the older people with whom we had worked. To this date, we have not returned to the communities (except once to Peccioli en route to other destinations), nor have we seen any of the members of the groups again.

We were sorry to leave the Bijlmer as, over the course of the project, we had built up a relationship with a community that was friendly and mutually enjoyable. We looked forward to our visits, and they welcomed our arrival. The design process itself was stimulating and provocative, encouraging the groups to engage with new ideas and find ways to express their reactions to us.

Ending the relationship after merely testing prototypes could seem unethical. The systems we designed – the Pastoral Radioscape for Peccioli, the Digital Boudoir for the Majorstua, and the Bijlmer's Projected Realities – all promised new opportunities for the older people to engage with each other, their neighbours and their environments. Yet after the project was over, none of the communities were left with physical realisations of the systems we had so idealistically proposed.

Presence did produce effects that seemed likely to outlive the project itself. At the outset of the final trial in the Bijlmer, for instance, a party was held in honour of the older people, and throughout the week, the group became the centre of attention for other inhabitants as members explained the pieces and the intention of the system as a whole. Local and national press covered the event, and became interested in new stories about the group's lives and current situations. By the time we left, a number of the older people were actively engaged in new projects of their own. It wasn't clear that they even noticed our departure.

So if no physical traces were left behind from the Presence project, we believe it did leave behind ideas and experiences that were beneficial to the groups. Like a workshop, an exhibition, or a theatrical event, the process through which we led them changed how they perceived their lives and circumstances, encouraging them to reflect and perhaps act on the insights and ideas that emerged. It may be regrettable that we could not continue to support the older people – but it may also be a form of 'benevolent ageism' to assume that such support was needed.

Perverse though it may seem, it would be a positive outcome if the older people did miss the systems we proposed and their engagement with the project. Beyond the specific products we developed, our work in Presence was meant to suggest ways that technologies might reflect richer versions of our lives. If people were unhappy that the story ended, they might question why technology does not tell a great many more such stories.

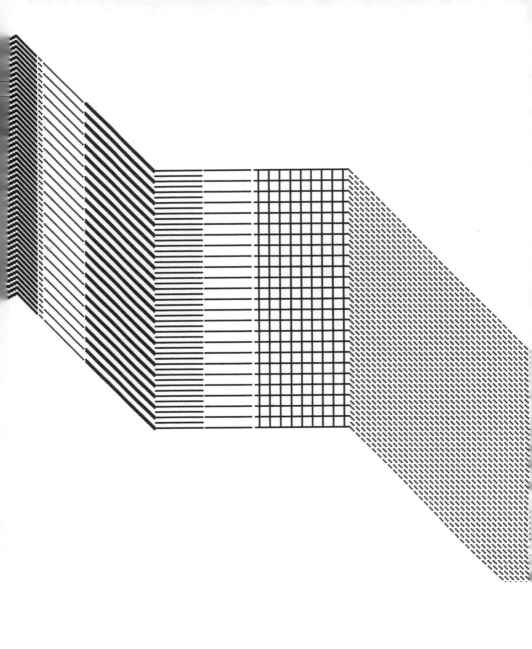

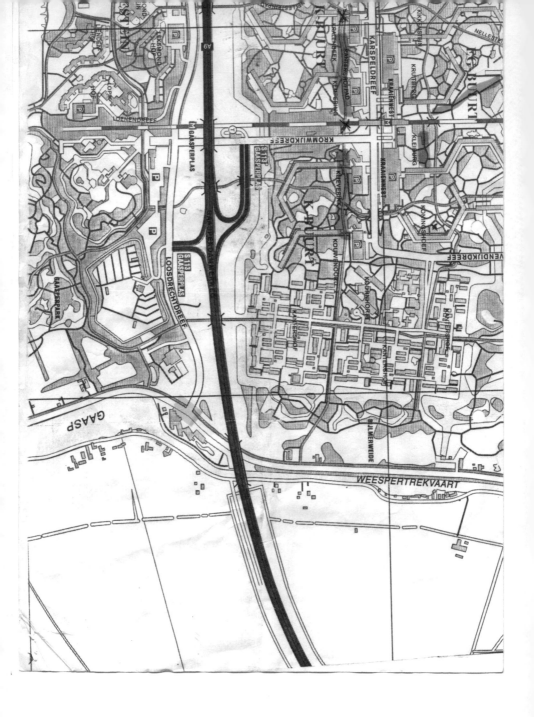

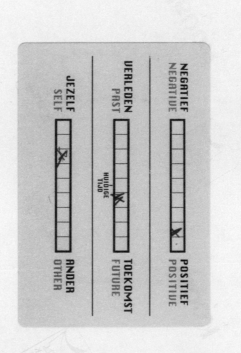

TRANSMITTER	TRASMITTENTE
RECEIVER	RICEVENTE
AERIAL	ADJ. AEREO N. ANTENNA
BATTERY	PILA (IN WATCH) (IN CAR: BATTERIA)
ANTENNA	ANTENNA
RADIOSCAPE	PANORAMA DELLE ONDE RADIO
DEVICE	STRUMENTO / ACCORGIMENTO TECNICO
LISTENING DEVICE	STRUMENTO DI ASCOLTO
SOCIAL	SOCIALE
PASTORAL	RURALE
TOURISM	TURISMO
RADIO TOURISM	RADIOTURISMO
LISTENING FURNITURE	
SONIC	(ADJ : DEL SUONO) ACUSTICO
SONIC LAY-BY	SITO DI ASCOLTO
AUDIO	AUDIO
CHANNEL	CANALE
TUNEABLE	REGOLABILE (PER QUANTO RIGUARDA LE FREQUENZE)
SOUNDSCAPE	PANORAMA DEI SUONI
SOUNDSCAPE MAP	MAPPA DEI SUONI
MICROPHONE	MICROFONO
COMMUNICATION	COMUNICAZIONE
RADIO BEACON	SEGNALE RADIO
BEACON	SEGNALE
LANDSCAPE	PANORAMA
RADIO LANDSCAPE	PANORAMA DELLE ONDE (FREQUENZE) RADIO
SOUNDSCAPE	
SOUNDSCAPE MAP	
TUNER	REGOLATORE DELLE FREQUENZE / TUNER
CAR RADIO TUNER	REGOLATORE DELLE FREQUENZE DELLE AUTORADIO

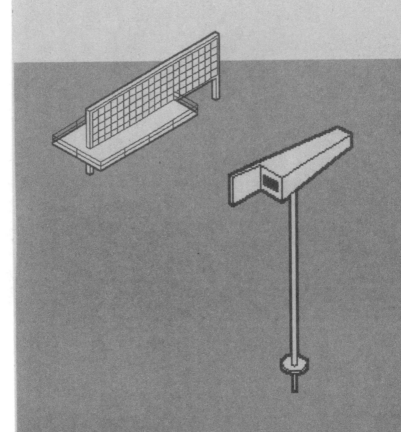

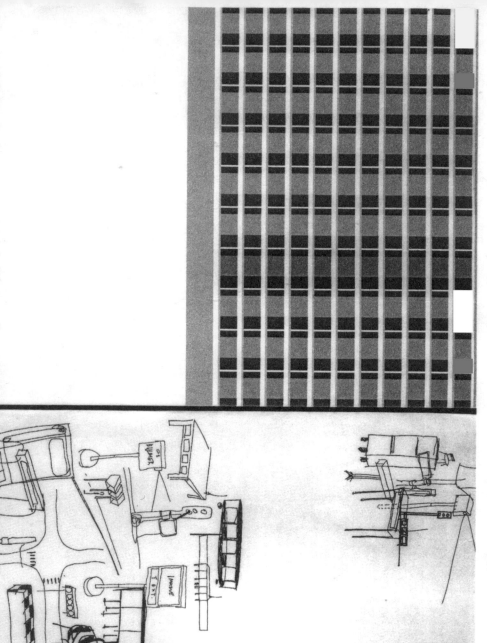

flat A-01	flat B-01	flat C-01
flat A-02	flat B-02	flat C-02
flat A-03	flat B-03	flat C-03
flat A-04	flat B-04	flat C-04
flat A-05	flat B-05	flat C-05
flat A-06	flat B-06	flat C-06
flat A-07	flat B-07	flat C-07
flat A-08	flat B-08	flat C-08
flat A-09	flat B-09	flat C-09
flat A-10	flat B-10	flat C-10
flat A-11	flat B-11	flat C-11

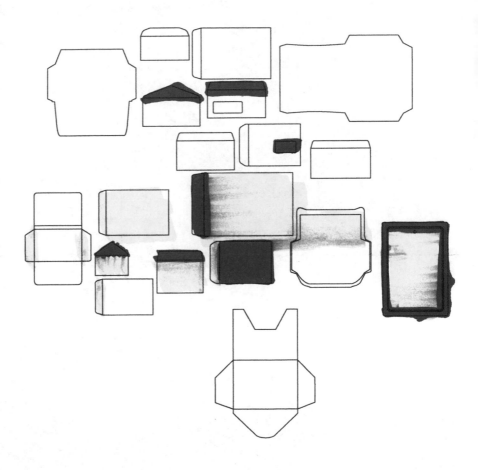

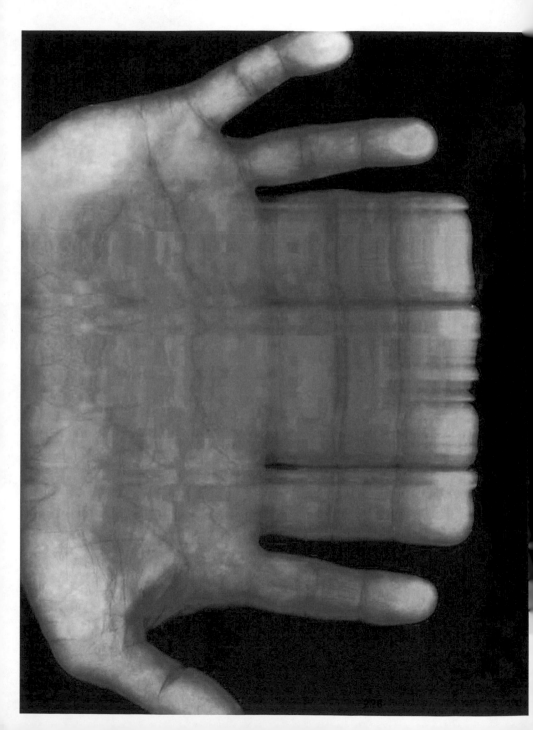

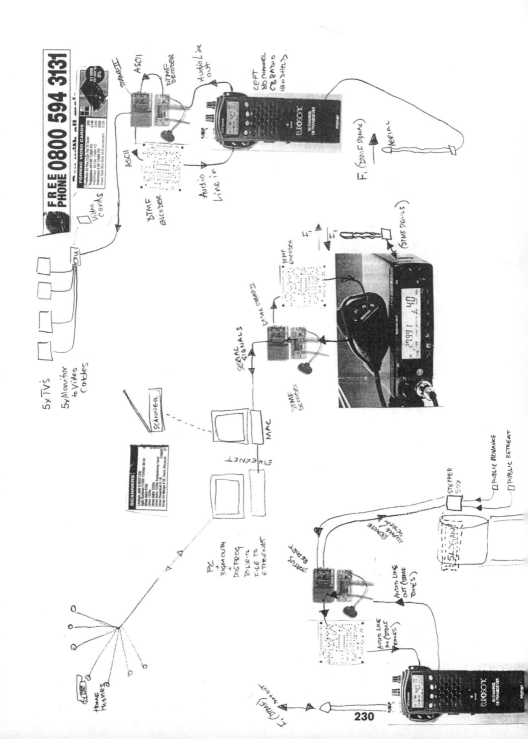

Video Cards

STAMP II

ASCII

DTMF DECODER

Audio Line Out

CEPT 80 CHANNEL CB RADIO HANDHELD

F₁ (DTMF SIGNAL)

AERIAL

ASCII

DTMF ENCODER

Audio Line in

5x TV's

5x Monitor to Video Cables

TV

DTMF ENCODER

$-F_1$

$-F_1$

(DTMF SIGNALS)

STAMP II

SERIAL SIGNALS

DTMF DECODER

2499 40

SCANNER

MAC

ETHERNET

SCANNERS

PC
+
BIGMOUTH
+
DOSTPROG
TO LOG IN
TO RS232
FILE TO ETHERNET

HOME PHONES

STATUS RETREAT

REMOTE ADVANCE RETREAT

STEPPER SOL

PUBLIC ADVANCE

PUBLIC RETREAT

SLICING

AUDIO LINE OUT (DTMF TONES)

AUDIO LINE IN (DTMF TONES)

F_1 (DTMF) In and Out

References

Andreotti, L. and Costa, X. (eds.), *Situationists: Art, Politics, Urbanism*. Museo d'Art Contemporani de Barcelona, 1996.

Archis magazine (March 1997), Special issue on the Bijlmer.

Aristotle. *Poetics* (Trans. S. H. Butcher). New York: Dover, 1997

Eysenck, M., and Kean, M. *Cognitive Psychology*. Hove: Erlbaum, 1995.

Field, S. *The screenwriter's workbook*. New York: Dell, 1988.

Gregory, R. L. (ed). *Oxford Companion to the Mind*. Oxford: Oxford University Press, 1987.

Hill, J. *The cat's whisker: 50 years of wireless design*. London: Oresko Books, 1978.

Hofmeester, K., and Saint Germain, E. C. *Presence: New media for older people*. Netherlands Design Institute, 1999.

Levy, J. *Surrealism*. First printed by Black Sun Press in 1936; reprinted by Da Capo Press, 1995.

Lindsay, P. H., & Norman, D. A. *Human Information Processing*. New York: Academic Press, 1977.

Plant, S. *The Most Radical Gesture: The Situationist International in a Postmodern Age*. London: Routledge, 1992.

Rumelhart, D. L., McClelland, J. L., & The PDP Research Group. *Parallel Distributed Processing (Vol. 1, Foundations)*. Cambridge, Massachusetts: MIT Press, 1986.

Sherman, C. *Untitled film stills*. Munich: Schirmer Art Books, 1998.

Strauss, N. *Radiotext(e)*. New York: Semiotext(e), 1993.

Van Bruggen, C. *John Baldessari*. New York, N.Y.: Rizzoli International Publications, 1990.

White, T. H. *United States early radio history*. www.ipass.net/~whitetho/